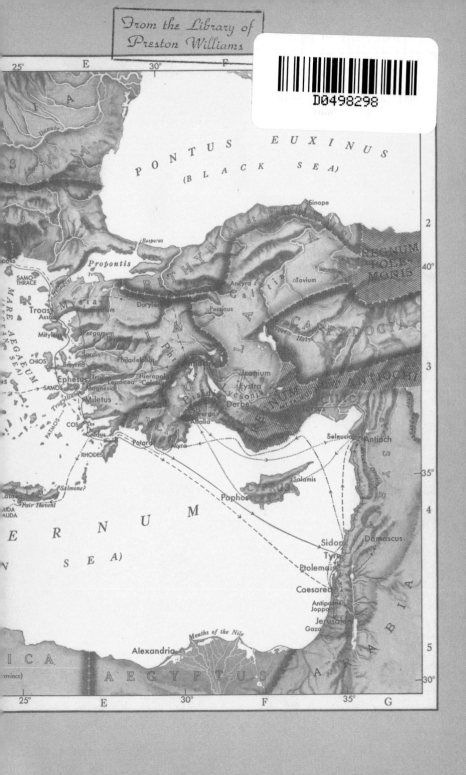

From the Library of
Preston Williams

D0498298

25°   E   30°   F

PONTUS   EUXINUS

(BLACK   SEA)

Sinope

Danube

Bosporus

Propontis

SAMO-
THRACE

BITHYNIA et PONTUS

Ancyra   Galatia   Tavium

Troas   Mysia   Dorylaeum

Assos   Adramyttium   Pessinus

Mitylene   Pergamum   Thyatira

MARE
AEGAEUM   Sardis   Philadelphia

(AEGEAN
SEA)   CHIOS   Smyrna

Ephesus   Tralles   Hierapolis

SAMOS   Magnesia   Laodicea   Colossae

Miletus

Trogyllium

PATMOS

COS

Cnidus

RHODES

Salmone?

Fair Havens

UDA
CAUDA

Iconium

Lystra

Iaconia

Derbe

Pisidia

Perga

Attalia

Patara   Myra

LYCIA

CAPPADOCIA

fluv Halys

Tarsus   CILICIA

Seleucia   Antioch

CYPRUS   Salamis

Paphos

ERNUM

SEA)

Sidon   Damascus

Tyre

Ptolemais

Caesarea

Antipatris
Joppa

Jerusalem   ARABIA

Gaza

Mouths of the Nile

Alexandria

ICA

(province)

AEGYPTUS   ARABIA

25°   E   30°   F   35°   G

40°

2

3

35°

4

5

30°

From the Library of
Preston Williams

Conqueror in Chains

A STORY OF THE APOSTLE PAUL

From the Library of
Preston Williams

Conqueror in Chains

A Story of the Apostle Paul

By DONALD G. MILLER

ILLUSTRATED BY ALBERT DeMEE JOUSSET

From the Library of
Preston Williams

The Westminster Press

PHILADELPHIA

COPYRIGHT, MCMLI, BY W. L. JENKINS

All rights reserved—no part of this book may be reproduced in any form without permission in writing from the publisher, except by a reviewer who wishes to quote brief passages in connection with a review written for magazine or newspaper.

In addition to the King James Version of the Scriptures quoted in this book, there will also be found quotations from *Letters to Young Churches,* by J. B. Phillips, copyright, 1947, by The Macmillan Company and used with their permission; *The New Testament Letters,* Prefaced and Paraphrased by J. W. C. Wand, published in 1946 by the Oxford University Press and used with their permission; the American Standard Edition of the Revised Bible and the Revised Standard Version of the New Testament, copyright, 1929 and 1946, respectively, by the International Council of Religious Education and used by permission.

Printed in the United States of America
at The Lakeside Press
R. R. Donnelley & Sons Company, Chicago
and Crawfordsville, Indiana

Contents

ABOUT THIS BOOK

THIS *is the story of the apostle Paul; and it is based, for the most part, on the books of the New Testament that give information about him—The Acts and the letters of Paul. These books, however, tell nothing of the boyhood of the man from Tarsus, nor how he met his death; neither do they supply sufficient details to give a complete biography. For the sake of this story, therefore, the first and last years of his life have been imaginatively reconstructed. Many details, too, have been added in recounting the known events of his career, based on knowledge of the ancient world and the peoples among whom Paul worked. Every effort has been expended to make the entire story consistent with what the New Testament tells about Paul. The Scripture passages on which this story is based are given in an index at the end of the book.*

DONALD G. MILLER

PART ONE

The Conqueror

CHAPTER 1

Ready for Action

THE HOUR was late. Shortened flames moved lazily about the mouths of the lamps, and smoke curled from their tips as the oil ran low. The streets of Jerusalem were quiet. In an upper room of a certain house heavy curtains, drawn close, marked the secrecy of a meeting charged tense with argument. A committee of Pharisees were deciding the fate of the followers of Jesus.

"We must be cautious," came the gentle voice of an elderly man.

His finely shaped lips were barely visible between a long, flowing beard and mustache.

"Let us wait for the verdict of time," he continued, "and make sure we do not happen to be fighting against God."

"It is to fight *for* God that *I* plead," countered the young man who was taking the lead in debate.

The argument was proving that the slight, wiry body of the younger man housed a mind and spirit remarkable both in depth and intensity. His features, taken separately, were almost ugly; but lighted up by the fire of his personality they became so fascinating that the group could hardly take their eyes from him. His mind, like a rapier, cut quickly to the heart of the issue in question. And his voice, though not natively pleasant, under the power of emotion carried irresistible conviction.

"Is it not written in the law," argued young Saul, " 'Cursed is every one that hangeth upon a tree'? Did not this Jesus hang from a tree? Yet these men call him Messiah, Gamaliel! Messiah!"

There were some who squirmed uneasily to see a young rabbi turn Scripture against his master, but the rush of words continued.

"To call a crucified criminal 'Messiah' is blasphemy! How are they better than he? It was with your consent that he died. So must they!"

"But his followers hold the law sacred," remonstrated Gamaliel. "He flouted it and cursed our tradition. They obey it, and they worship daily in the Temple."

Nodding heads showed support for the older man, and he went on: "They are strange, but harmless. Let time and God be their judge. If they are of God, it is neither right nor possible to silence them. If they are not of God, God himself will judge them."

But Saul understood the followers of the Nazarene better than did Gamaliel. And better even than some of those followers themselves he knew how completely they had forsaken the old Jewish faith.

"They worship at the Temple only as propagandists for their faith," he said. "Have you listened to them, Gamaliel? They announce daily that this accursed criminal Jesus is God's

Holy One! They hold up the God of Israel to ridicule in the eyes of the Romans by claiming that this despised felon was Israel's King. Can the God of Israel be slandered and we fail to act?"

"But to move against them is to move against ourselves," came Gamaliel's rebuttal. "Some of the Pharisees are numbered among them, and they believe as we do in the resurrection of the dead."

The old rabbi had seen false messiahs come and go. He had seen their armed rebellions put down with bloody force, and in his eyes the new movement was harmless by comparison.

"They abhor political revolution, as we do," he continued. "Their enthusiasm may turn aside some of the Zealots, who would bring Israel to ruin by arming secretly for revolution against Rome. Time will cure their folly about this false messiah and destroy their hope of his return."

"But it is the excellencies you mention that make them dangerous," came Saul's quick reply. "Half-truths spread faster than whole truths. It is their virtues that blind men to the real danger. They are not smoldering embers that will die out in time. They are rather smoking kindling, about to burst into flames, which can consume the house of our faith. They keep the law through custom, but it is not vital to their faith. I have heard them teach. If they prevail, the law is dead! We must stamp out this movement quickly, or play traitor to God! Compromise will mean death to the way of the Jews."

It became obvious that Saul was winning his case. Those who at first had been reluctant to side against Gamaliel because of his age and reputation, gradually fell under the spell of Saul's arguments. He was not so seasoned by experience as was Gamaliel; but he grasped real issues that Gamaliel had failed to see. Who could deny that he was right? Even Gamaliel began to weaken as Saul pointed out clearly that loyal Jews and believers in Jesus could not live long in agreement.

The case was decided in every mind as Saul ended his plea:

"God do so to me, and more also, if I be not willing to risk my life to exterminate this ungodly teaching from the earth!"

After that the group turned readily to practical plans for combating the followers of Jesus. To Saul this seemed to be his hour of destiny. As Elijah had arisen to save Israel from the idolatry of Jezebel, so he felt raised up to save his people from monstrous worship of a crucified criminal. Saul's birth, his native genius, his training, his experience—all these things led him to champion the faith of his fathers and to become the reasonable choice for leader of the persecution.

It had been no common day in the life of the wealthy Jewish home in Tarsus when Saul was born. Until then, one deep shadow had darkened the household. Wealth and prestige among Jews and Gentiles were theirs. They were full citizens both in Tarsus and in Rome. They were also Pharisees and took great pride in their religion. But there was no son. In Israel this was a disgrace.

The cloud lifted when Saul was born! "Blessed be God," said his father fervently when the birth was announced, "who has taken away our reproach and given us a son."

Relatives and friends poured in with congratulations and gifts—costly gifts the value of which was exceeded only by the joy of parents whose deepest wish had been fulfilled. When, eight days later, a host gathered to celebrate the naming of the child through the Jewish rite of circumcision, there were greater festivities than that home had ever witnessed. In the midst of chanting and prayers led by a priest, the child was given the name of Israel's first king, Saul. And since his status as a freeborn Roman also must be indicated in his name, he was, as a Roman, to be called Paul.

Saul's boyhood home bore all the marks of wealth. His family for several generations had been profitably active in the never-ending stream of commerce that flowed through Tarsus. Although extravagance was outlawed by the rigorous outlook of Pharisees, Saul's family suffered no lack of comforts which life in Tarsus could afford. In spite of the fact that by the time Saul was grown Jewish religious convictions had drawn fixed social lines between him and Gentile young people, he grew up with a distinct sense of his family's superior social position.

Religion was the very breath of Saul's childhood years. Each day began with the repetition of the Shema:

"Hear, O Israel: The Lord our God is one Lord: and thou shalt love the Lord thy God with all thine heart, and with all thy soul, and with all thy might."

Before breakfast the family gathered in a chamber adjoining the dining room where sat several large earthen jars of water and some small containers filled with perfumed oil. Using a dipper, Saul's father reverently poured onto his hands a small amount of water, then held them up for the water to run down as far as the wrists, as a symbol of purification preceding the meal. This done, some of the perfumed oil was rubbed into his hands, face, beard, and hair. Each member of the family followed a similar ritual.

"Blessed is He who brings forth bread from the earth," began the prayer that opened every meal; and longer prayers of thanks were made as each meal ended.

A mezuzah hung above the lintel of the door into Saul's home. This was a little parchment scroll, encased in a metal holder, on which were written statements of Israel's faith. As Saul passed through the door, he always touched the mezuzah, then kissed the finger that had touched it. This silently witnessed his belief that the God of Israel preserved his "going out" and his "coming in."

Saul's home also had a complete copy of the Jewish Scriptures, which only the well-to-do could afford. Nightfall found him and his sister snuggled beside their father to hear bedtime stories from the Sacred Writings. Abraham, Jacob, Joseph, Moses, Samson, and David were their childhood heroes. From the time Saul was three years old his father began to teach him short selections from the Scriptures and simple prayers.

The most solid fact of Saul's early life was *God*.

The weekly Sabbath riveted the young Saul's religious convictions. Late Friday evening his mother lighted the Sabbath lamp, a flame kept burning throughout the twenty-four Sabbath hours. Neither work nor extensive journeys were undertaken. A special feast, to which guests were frequently invited, inaugurated the Sabbath on Friday evening.

"Blessed art thou, O God," prayed Saul's father, as they gathered to eat, "for the gift of the holy Sabbath." This day was a sign of God's love for Israel forever.

The following morning found the entire family at the synagogue. Saul and his father entered one door, his mother and sister another. Inside, the women were separated from the men by a wooden screen, where they could hear but could not be seen. At the center, near the front, was an elevated platform on which stood a reading desk and chest, or "ark," in which the sacred scrolls were kept.

As the service opened, the ruler of the synagogue chose a member from the congregation to lead the worship.

"Blessed be thou, O Lord, King of the world," the leader began, "who formest the light and createst the darkness."

"Amen," swelled from the congregation.

The Shema, which had expressed the faith of forty generations of devout Hebrews, was repeated and followed by a benediction.

The leader then moved over before the ark to present the prayers of the congregation to God in the form of eighteen time-honored liturgical prayers, to each of which the congregation made a response.

If a Levite were present, the formal prayers were concluded with the ancient benediction of Aaron:

"The Lord bless thee, and keep thee:

   The Lord make his face shine upon thee, and be gracious
      unto thee:

The Lord lift up his countenance upon thee, and give thee
peace."

At this point an attendant took the scroll of the Law and the
Prophets from the "ark" and presented it to the leader of the
worship. The section of the Law prescribed for the day was
read, followed by a paragraph from the Prophets. A sermon
concluded the service.

The presence of a distinguished-looking family group seated
near the rear of the synagogue sharpened the religious strug-
gles of Saul's early years. These people were Gentiles, not Jews.
They had abandoned idols for the worship of the one true God.
They were faithful attendants at the synagogue. But they had
not been circumcised, nor did they keep the ceremonies of the
law of Moses.

"Does God love such people as these?" Saul wondered.

"Can they be acceptable to God without becoming Jews?"

"How can Jewish religion best live in a pagan world—by
mixing with 'God fearers' such as these or by breaking with
them entirely, in strict loyalty to ancient Jewish tradition?"
Such questions as these rose to disturb him.

The problem was deepened through Saul's friendship with
Lucius, the son in this family. Both boys had a genius for
friendship, but Lucius did not take religion half so seriously
as did Saul.

"Are you out of prison now?" asked Lucius, as the two boys
met one day outside the synagogue.

Saul knew that this was a friendly gibe at him, because the
ceremonies of the feast week just ended had made it impossible
for him to mix with the Gentiles.

"You wouldn't call a holiday imprisonment, would you?"
Saul shrugged off Lucius' remark.

"You might as well have been in jail for all we have seen of
you," came the answer. "I suppose Moses himself would have
been proud of you this week."

At this Saul flushed. His friendship for Lucius was deep. But jesting about his religion was something he could not endure.

"Someday the world will be proud of Moses," he retorted. "The day will come when the Jews will rule the world."

"I should fare well then," replied Lucius. "I'll tell them I am a friend of yours. That should get me by."

Saul's eyes flashed a deep-seated fire. The hot blood of centuries of Jewish religious passion made his face crimson. Losing self-control, he lashed out at Lucius with words he had read from the most fanatical rabbis:

"When Messiah comes, all men will swear allegiance. If not, he will make their flesh rot away while they are standing on their feet, their eyes shall rot in their sockets, and their tongue shall rot within their mouth!"

Lucius was used to Saul's quick retorts, but he saw he had prodded him too much this time. He tried to change the subject. Saul too began to feel sheepish over his outburst. There was an embarrassed pause, in which both boys awkwardly sought to apologize to each other without words. The tension was eased by the call of their parents to go home.

"The city has not seen us for a while," risked Lucius, before going. "Shall we give it the benefit of our presence tomorrow?"

"I don't object to paying it such a compliment," Saul retorted.

"Then I'll see you at midmorning at your father's business house," called Lucius as he moved off. "My father says the wharf is crowded with ships. There may be some we have never seen before."

The next morning the two were off. And what a city Tarsus was to interest boys! The excellent inland harbor, well protected from both high seas and pirates, attracted the commerce of the world. A direct road through the lowest pass across the mighty Taurus Mountains led into the interior of Asia Minor. A half day's excursion around the wharves and streets of Tarsus was like a trip around the world. Ships of all descriptions, people of all nationalities, commerce of all sorts flowed through

Tarsus in a never-ending stream. Armed soldiers and shrewd tax collectors from Rome, wily merchants from Sidon, bearded rabbis from Judea, skilled craftsmen from Cyprus, learned philosophers from Athens, colorful magicians from Persia, seductive dancing girls from Egypt—what had the world that Tarsus did not have?

The river front lured the boys first. A host of little galleys tied to the shore moved gently to the tread of loudmouthed stevedores, loading and unloading. In and out of these boats went wares from the corners of the earth. Grain trickled over the edges of deep scoops. Knotted, smelly wool, looking little like the sheep that recently had carried it, was bundled off. Huge rolls of tent canvas, made of goats' hair from the hills above Tarsus, bent men low. Spices filled the air with the aroma of an Oriental bazaar. The great forests of the Taurus Mountains lay there, stripped of leaves, bark, and branches— huge hand-hewn beams and sturdy planks. Arabian dates and figs, Egyptian oils and wines, pottery from Palestine—Tarsus stretched her fingers to the markets of the world, then closed her hand and brought them all together in her palm.

"Look at that neat little galley from Rome," said Lucius. "I wonder how long it took to make the trip. Wouldn't I like to be master of a vessel like that!"

"That's too small and too slow to suit me," answered Saul. "When I go to sea, I want to command one of those sailboats that don't get up here, one of the big ones which dock down at the main harbor."

A queer little ship, with Egyptian gods carved on her prow, brought up the question whether they would rather go to Rome or to Alexandria. Before a decision was reached, both decided that before they died they would most surely visit both places.

Saul and Lucius became in imagination world travelers. The coasts of Greece, Italy, Spain, North Africa, Palestine, and Syria seemed to flit before their eyes. They talked about the

most famous galley that had ever come up the Cydnus River
to dock on the very spot where they stood. Their grandfathers
had seen it—the galley on which Cleopatra, stretched full
length like a goddess, had come to subdue Antony with her
charms. Flutes and harps had sent soft music along the river
front. Incense had perfumed the air. Under a golden canopy,
dressed like Venus, with young boys and girls as cupids and
graces fanning her and plying the oars, the wily queen had
staged the most colorful arrival the long history of Tarsus had
ever witnessed. How these boys envied their grandfathers the
privilege of seeing that! They dreamed too of the days when
Cilicia was a hotbed of pirates. Tales came to mind of many
an ancient sea raider—names that were household words—who
had wrought terror in small barks off the Tarsian coast until
the Romans finally put an end to large-scale piracy.

The boys moved on down the river front to where Lucius'
father kept a skiff tied up. Slipping into it, they rowed down
the river toward the main harbor. On the way many magnificent buildings fronting the river loomed into view—theaters,
libraries, temples, hotels, public baths with their gardens, and,
above all, the world-famous university.

Before long they reached the harbor. It was a lake, fed by
natural springs, dredged out to a great depth suitable for the
largest ships, into which the Tarsians had turned the course of
the river. This marvelous feat of engineering had given Tarsus
an advantage over rival cities, and had been a large factor in
establishing it as the center of commerce for that whole region.
Here they rowed around among the boats docked at the large
wharves on three sides of the broad harbor and saw duplicated
on a larger scale what they had seen on the riverbank in the
heart of the city.

From the harbor, as they looked back toward the city, they
could see the foothills just beyond. The snow-capped heights
of Taurus rose majestically into the sky about thirty miles in
the distance. The little white dots on one of the ridges were

homes in the hills, where the families of both Saul and Lucius spent their summers, for the intense heat of the Tarsian plain was almost unbearable during the hot season. On a plateau near the homes was the city stadium, where athletic contests were featured during the summer months.

Beyond that, to the north, where the river dropped rapidly and flowed swiftly, lay the famous Cilician Gates. These marked the spot where the river had cut a deep gorge through the solid rock formation of the mountains. The Tarsians, in order to open travel through that gorge, had dug out the solid rock on one side of the river channel to make a good road. This second engineering feat had further enabled the Tarsian people to outstrip rival cities, for the Cilician Gates opened by all odds the most passable route across the Taurus Mountains, and secured the permanent position of Tarsus as the leading trade center for all Asia Minor. Saul, to the end of his days, was proud to be a citizen of Tarsus, "a very famous city."

As the afternoon wore on, the boys rowed their bark back to the dock. The religious discussion of the day before had not been resumed, for each boy was reluctant to mar the happiness of the other, and the sights and sounds of the great city of nearly a half million people had been too intriguing for serious talk. Walking together to the turning that led to the Jewish quarter of the city, they parted to go to their own homes.

"What claimed your interest today, Saul?" asked his father that evening.

"The river and the harbor, Father," replied Saul. "The docks were as full as I have ever seen them. The wealth of the world floated on the waters of Tarsus today."

"My son, your eagerness for those wharves would mark you as either a sailor or a merchant," remarked his father. "But we desire you, and you have chosen, to be a rabbi. You will sail the seas of knowledge, and trade with the merchandise of truth, which is more precious than gold."

"That is my highest ambition," replied Saul.

"The day is not far off, my boy. You will soon be ready to study Jewish doctrine with the rabbis. You know our custom. Reading at five. Memorizing oral tradition at ten. Now at thirteen you are nearly ready, not only to memorize the ancient precepts, but to reason about them, explain them, and apply them to our time. Your mother and I have decided to give you the best training there is. You are to go to Jerusalem to study with the great rabbi Gamaliel."

"Jerusalem!" cried Saul, his face lighting up and his hands clenched in excitement. "Jerusalem! To sit at the feet of Gamaliel! Do you mean it, Father?"

"Yes, my son, I mean it. But you know you must learn a trade before you go. We Jews do not tolerate indolence. Furthermore, our history is drenched with hate and persecution for our faith. We never know what the future may hold. Rome may disown us at any time. You must be able to provide for yourself under any circumstances. Our rabbis say, 'He that teacheth not his son a trade does the same as if he taught him to be a thief.' "

At the age of thirteen, therefore, Saul was apprenticed to a tentmaker. For two years he learned to weave and shape and sew the tough canvas called *Cilicium*, made out of the long hair of the goats which were herded on the Cilician hills. He worked hard learning this trade, and, with his unusual vigor and intelligence, soon came to excel as a workman. Indeed, he could turn out as worthy work as those who had toiled at the trade for years.

At fifteen he was ready to go to Jerusalem. It was a marvelous prospect for a boy of his deep patriotism and intense religious nature. At times during those two years of working, it hardly seemed possible that his fond hopes were to become reality. It all seemed like a dream.

There was but one thing to mar his joy. The discussion he had had with Lucius outside the synagogue door had been renewed several times. After each dispute Saul felt the pangs of

inner struggle deepen. There were times, in moments of weakness, when he almost persuaded himself that he was wrong in
his undivided loyalty to the Jewish law. Perhaps what the Jews
had to offer the world could best be given by coming to terms
with the Greeks and Romans. Why not break down ancient
custom? Why not fit Jewish religion into Greek philosophy?
Why go off to Jerusalem to study, when one of the most famous
universities in the world was right at his door? Did Gamaliel
have as much to offer as Athenodorus, the world-renowned
tutor of the emperor Augustus?

Saul hated himself for being swayed by Gentile arguments
which he felt could not be true, and which to him seemed blasphemous. To avoid surrender, he became more fanatical. He
told himself over and over again that although he might not
be able to argue the case with final proof, when he got to Jerusalem Gamaliel would give him all the answers.

For Saul, the die was cast. He was to be a Pharisee of the
Pharisees, a strict member of the strictest sect of the Jews. He
would give all he had to his people. Someday Messiah would
come and deliver them. He would establish them as the rulers
of the earth.

So, when Saul bade Lucius farewell, although a surge of the
old warmth of friendship arose at parting, yet he felt deeply
that leaving Lucius was leaving temptation. He set out for the
Holy City of his fathers to outdo all his compatriots in loyalty
to the Jewish law and devotion to the Jewish cause. All he was
and all he had belonged exclusively to the God of the Jews. He
would serve him entirely, with no reservations, or die trying.

After a round of feasts and farewells, the exciting day
came when he set his face toward Jerusalem. "Tarsus," Saul's
thoughts were saying, "thou art a very famous city. But I go
to a city more famous—the city of David, the spiritual capital
of the world. And one day, when Messiah comes, Jerusalem
will exchange places with Rome. O Lord, Redeemer of Israel,
speed the coming of that day!"

CHAPTER 2

Pursued

THE MOMENT Saul caught sight of the gold-covered dome of the Temple, he knew for the first time what the ancient Hebrew poet meant when he wrote:

> "If I forget thee, O Jerusalem,
>   Let my right hand forget her skill.
>   Let my tongue cleave to the roof of my mouth."

Every stone in Jerusalem was eloquent with history and with hope. Roman slavery was lightened by the memory of glorious days now gone—yet not gone in the hearts of devout Jews. Roman outrages were endured in the hope of a more glorious day still to come, when Messiah should redeem Israel and make it supreme among the nations. Jerusalem was the one surviving

24

link between the glories of the past and the hopes of the future. When Saul looked for the first time on this place, it was the most tremendous moment he had yet experienced.

Then with what awe Saul met Gamaliel, Jerusalem's greatest teacher! He was a kindly man, both revered and loved by his students. He was the leader of the group of Pharisees who were less bitter than others toward the Gentiles. Hate and violence he deplored. Yet he was a Pharisee. And with Pharisees religion was serious business.

"All men are evil," Gamaliel taught. "They are born that way." This was familiar teaching to Saul. He had absorbed it from the synagogue at Tarsus.

"The one end in life is to become right with God," the teaching continued. "The one way to do that is to keep the Jewish law. To observe its minute regulations each day without missing a jot or tittle is the only way to gain God's favor."

This too was not unknown to Saul. But on the lips of Gamaliel at Jerusalem it had a different ring. Judaism in Jerusalem was severe and intolerant.

Outside the Holy Land, where the Jews were a minority, their difference from Gentiles sometimes was stressed as little as possible. Gentile ridicule made this necessary. The Greeks and Romans could not understand the Jews. The refusal to eat pork they interpreted as giving divine honors to swine. The keeping of the Sabbath they attributed to laziness. Worshiping without images they felt was worshiping nothing—it was atheism. To correct these misunderstandings, and to win converts, the Jews living outside the Holy Land often courted Gentile favor by every means open to them.

But Judaism in Jerusalem was different. Religious customs were observed more strictly. Jewish peculiarities were magnified rather than diminished. The urge to get along with the Gentiles was offset by scorn for the Gentiles. Especially did the Pharisees insist that it was only by the most careful observance of the law that the way could be prepared for Messiah to come.

And Messiah would destroy Gentile opposition and deliver his people.

As Saul breathed the pure air of Pharisaism in Jerusalem, he became deeply convinced of its truth. Why had Messiah delayed so long in coming? Was it not because the Jews had been disloyal to the law? The faith had been frittered away in compromise. Compromise became to him a dangerous threat to the very existence of his faith. Judaism's only hope lay in separating itself from every concession to the Gentiles.

With a quick mind, with a religious nature, with a will like iron, Saul set out to test Pharisaism. If zealously keeping the law made a man righteous, he would be righteous. If his absolute commitment to God would hasten Messiah's coming, he would further that end.

Rapidly, under Gamaliel's guidance, Saul outstripped his fellow students. No tinge of moderation, not even the restraints of common sense, tamed his enthusiasm. He memorized the Scriptures. He crammed his mind full of the traditions of the rabbis. He tested every action by its conformity to the letter of the minutest law. From before dawn each day until he threw his weary body on his pallet at night, Saul drove himself relentlessly toward perfection, both in study and in religious observances. He was keen in reasoning, ruthless in debate, and fanatical in devotion. He stood in a class by himself, without a peer.

Shortly after his arrival in Jerusalem, Saul hunted out the synagogue of the Cilicians. This synagogue had been established by Jews from the region of Tarsus who had come to Jerusalem to live, and with them Saul felt at home. He spoke their language. He knew their world. Before long he became a frequent leader of worship and a chief figure in the lively discussions held there. His fame as a student made the Cilicians proud of him. His renown made their synagogue renowned.

For several years, as a student, Saul tasted the delights of success and public approval.

"A saint!" men glanced at each other as they passed him on the street.

"Another Gamaliel in the making!"

"The deliverance of Israel would not long be delayed if enough Jews kept the law like that."

But deep in Saul's heart there was no lasting satisfaction. His inner life was a continual storm. He believed that God was holy, and must punish all sin. The way to avoid God's punishment was to make one's self holy by doing all good works commanded in the law. But, try as he would, there were times when he failed in this endeavor.

Life became for him a bitter struggle. Two Sauls battled daily in the arena of his inner life. One fought for the right; the other enticed him to the wrong. He kept up a desperate hope that the champion of the right would win and gain a favorable verdict with the divine Judge at the end of life. But what if he should not? Then fearful judgment lay ahead.

The tenseness of his effort to keep the law produced an overwhelming fit of depression every time he failed. Although the failure may have been so small that a less honest person would not even have noticed it, he went through agonies of spirit. He resolved more deeply not to fail again. His increased effort made the next slip more torturing to his inner life.

Hope and despair, heroic effort and tragic failure, tossed his life back and forth between them. Like a moth caught in a spider's web, the more he struggled, the worse off he became. He had difficulty in sleeping. He lost weight. His face grew pallid, his features drawn. He became irritable. At times he was so depressed that he could do little but stare vacantly into space, saying to himself:

"Miserable wretch that I am! How shall I be delivered from this living death?"

Such inner struggle could have completely unbalanced a man of lesser stature than Saul. But he kept going through the amazing vitality of his own will and the promise he kept making to himself that when his days of training were over and he was embarked on his career as a rabbi, all would be well.

His years at Jerusalem ended, Saul went back to Tarsus to be a rabbi. The Jewish community there welcomed him with enthusiasm. His prowess as Gamaliel's prize pupil had long been heralded among Tarsus Jews. He had exceeded the high promise of his boyhood days. Now, in this city famous for its learning, the Jews had a teacher who could match wits with any of the pagan philosophers. He was greeted by his Jewish admirers almost as a conqueror returning from battle. Nor did he disappoint their hopes. No pagan ever attacked Moses in Tarsus without being routed by the wit, learning, and scorn of Saul. In debate he was a blazing menace to opponents. As a teacher he set forth the excellencies of the Mosaic law with unsurpassed skill.

Saul could have asked for nothing better in life than to spend the rest of his days as the leading rabbi of Tarsus—except to become the leading rabbi of Jerusalem. Gamaliel was in his prime and would likely last a long time yet. But when he died, would the opportunity come to take his place? Perhaps! In the meantime, Saul determined to make the best of his work at Tarsus. There he could correct the tendency to compromise with Gentiles, and could take up some of the slack with which the law was kept. If an opening in Jerusalem came in the distant future, he would be ready for it.

The occasion for him to go to Jerusalem, however, came sooner than he expected. News began to filter through to Tarsus concerning a strange Galilaean teacher named Jesus. He came from an obscure family. He was not trained in the rabbinic colleges of Jerusalem. He did not have the approval of the religious authorities. But he taught with originality and force, and had strange powers to heal diseased bodies and minds.

At first Saul was very curious. The strong hope of a coming

Messiah made any unusual religious event important. Saul's interest, however, was changed into hostility when fuller reports of Jesus' teachings reached him, for this man handled the law loosely. He defied the traditions of the rabbis. He openly denounced the Pharisees. He made claims which to Saul were blasphemous.

When, therefore, the news of the crucifixion of this new teacher came, Saul dismissed him as a false leader who had received his deserved punishment.

"The judgments of God are right," he said to himself. "Blasphemy deserves death."

Word from Jerusalem a few weeks later, however, disturbed Saul deeply. At the Feast of Pentecost a rough, uncouth Galilaean fisherman, acting like a drunken man, had stood in the Temple court and blasphemously claimed that this Jesus, who had been crucified, was Messiah. He claimed also that Jesus was alive. A great crowd of people at the Feast had believed this accursed teaching.

The Sanhedrin had called in the offenders and admonished them and beaten them, but still they continued to teach. Some felt that the action of the officials had not been decisive enough, and Saul was particularly distressed to learn of Gamaliel's counsel to let these men alone. How could Gamaliel permit men to teach that a criminal who had died a dog's death on a cross was Messiah?

Furthermore, Saul had heard that one named Stephen had been arguing this new teaching in his own beloved synagogue of the Cilicians, without successful contradiction.

"Has it come to such a pass that the God of Israel has no defenders?" he asked himself. "Surely that is not possible in Jerusalem! Why, then, has this false teaching not been dealt with more drastically?"

To his questions he could find no answers. He felt that his distance from the scene made it impossible for him to appraise the situation. But the reports that kept coming to him were so disturbing that he could not put his mind at rest. He decided, therefore, to go to Jerusalem to investigate at close range.

At Jerusalem, Saul traced with customary thoroughness every clue he could get that would give him a clear picture of the stirring events that had taken place during his absence.

Who was this Jesus? What was his background? What had he taught? How did he treat the law? Who were his followers? What did the leading rabbis think of him? Why had he been killed? What was there about him that gripped men so mightily that they could continue in the delusion that he was Messiah, even after his shameful death had completely disproved it? Who had first started this lie about his resurrection? Why had it not been silenced immediately?

Saul sharpened his opinion through personal knowledge of Jesus' followers. He listened to them preach in Solomon's porch at the Temple. He conversed with many of them in private. He even went to one of their common meals, or "love feasts." He observed closely their manner of life—their zeal, their love, the sharing of their goods with each other, their impassioned loyalty to Jesus, their certainty that he was alive.

Increasingly Saul saw in this movement a threat to the religion of his fathers. Judaism was based on keeping the law. This new religion was founded on the belief that a crucified fanatic was Messiah, and that after his crucifixion God had raised him from the dead. Both these beliefs were scandalous, and both meant the end of the law. True, these believers still kept the law through custom. But Saul saw clearly that this was incidental to their faith. The heart of their religion lay in loyalty to Jesus and in the mistaken notion that he was alive. Neither of these had anything to do with the law.

And their devotion and the mystic sense of power in their lives—these were the most dangerous features. They had blinded men to the real dangers of the movement and kept the authorities from taking drastic action. They also branded them as in league with the world of evil spirits. Satan could give men mysterious powers as well as God. Devils could parade as angels of light.

To Saul the issue was clear. Judaism must either destroy this new faith or be destroyed by it. The two could not long live together. He went, therefore, to the leaders of the Pharisees to open their eyes to this real threat to their faith. He would persuade them that they must fight fire with fire.

So it was that Saul and the leading men of Jerusalem were closeted together and taking counsel secretly. The counsel of Saul prevailed. The Pharisees laid aside the cautions of Gamaliel and decided upon a determined program of extermination. Saul's insight and passion made him the natural one to lead the effort to rid the world of this heresy. To him, therefore, the Sanhedrin delegated authority to destroy the believers in Jesus by whatever means might be found necessary.

Stephen was Saul's first target. He engaged in public dispute with him in the Cilician synagogue, in order to draw him out in clear, full statements for which he could be tried and condemned. Stephen was bold in his avowal that Jesus was Messiah. But he went beyond that. Jesus was not only the Messiah of the Jews; he was the Messiah of all men! Christianity was not a new brand of Judaism. It was a universal religion. It brought men to God without benefit of the Holy Land, the Jewish law, or the Temple.

In these statements Saul saw clearly his opportunity to secure Stephen's condemnation. To speak lightly of the Holy Land outraged the patriotism of the masses. They could, therefore, easily be persuaded to denounce Stephen. The Pharisees, on the other hand, however they differed among themselves, were fanatical in their devotion to the law. For Stephen to condemn the law was to unite all elements of the Pharisees against him. The Sadducees too, who as priests depended on exclusive control of the Temple worship, would gladly oppose Stephen. With no king, and no independent political life, the loyalties of the people centered in the Temple. It was the symbol of their hope. It was the one remaining visible witness to the glory of the God of Israel. When Messiah came, he would come suddenly to his Temple, and there establish his Kingdom. To denounce the Temple, then, was to destroy the position of the Sadducees and the hope of the nation at one blow.

Armed with this evidence, Saul laid his net to snare Stephen. He knew how easily the people could be incited to religious riot, for the preaching of Stephen was already a subject of public discussion. He laid careful plans, therefore, to arouse the passions of the populace on a suitable occasion, in order to secure Stephen's speedy condemnation. It was illegal to put a man to death without consent of the Romans, but if the mob could be worked into a frenzy, the deed could be done spontaneously, and the Romans would be unable to prevent it.

The blow soon fell. As Stephen was addressing a group in the shelter of Solomon's porch in the Temple area, strong men quickly surrounded and seized him. At the same time a bearded old man, highly venerated because of his age and devotion to the law, spoke to the crowd.

"Men of Israel, why do you listen to this man?" he cried. "Have you not heard his blasphemy against Moses and against God?"

"He is a good man," someone replied.

"He is God's prophet," came another voice from the crowd.

"Curses be on you and on him!" shouted the old man, raising his gnarled arms above his head. "He is a blasphemer! A son of the devil! He is worthy of death! If you listen to him, you are enemies of God!"

By this time the men who had seized Stephen began yelling. The ever-present crowds in the Temple court came running to the scene.

"Take him to the council," ordered the old man.

The mob surged across the Temple court toward the stone chamber where the Sanhedrin was in session.

As they crowded the entrance, the high priest who presided over the court could be seen sitting at the center of the great council hall. Around him on both sides, seated in a large semicircle, sat the rest of the seventy judges who made up the supreme court of the Jews.

The old man who had set off the riot strode across the marble floor with determined step, his face alive with anger. Behind him came Stephen in the grip of two strong men. This trio was flanked by the group of eight or ten men who had at first surrounded Stephen. The mob followed.

As the old man spoke, the crowd quieted and bent forward to listen. "We bring before you a blasphemer, worthy of death," he addressed the high priest.

"We have witnesses here who can take oath before God that they have heard him utter blasphemy."

"Let the witnesses speak," replied the high priest.

The first stepped forward:

"This fellow is continually speaking in the Temple court and in the synagogues against this holy Temple and against the law!"

Another spoke:

"We have heard him say that Jesus the Nazarene, who was condemned by this court and crucified by the Roman procurator, will destroy this Temple, and change the sacred customs handed down to us by Moses."

Seventy pairs of eyes converged on the face of Stephen. These were serious charges. Followers of Jesus had repeatedly been tried before the Sanhedrin, but never for these crimes. They had said that Jesus was Messiah. This could be dismissed as a mistake. They had said that Jesus was alive. This could be ruled out as hallucination. Mistakes and hallucinations were to be punished and suppressed, and they had been. But heretofore the followers of Jesus had worshiped in the Temple, and kept the law, and believed in the special privileges of those who dwelt in the Holy Land. To denounce the law, to deride the Temple, to demean the Holy Land—this was different. The air became charged. The moment was tense. The silence deepened.

As every eye in the chamber focused on Stephen, a strange sense of destiny seized him. Here was an opportunity to confess his faith before the leaders of the nation. He was not a defendant, but a witness. He was not on trial before them; they were on trial before God. He remembered how Jesus had witnessed before Pontius Pilate and these same Jewish leaders. A surge of fearlessness swept through him. He was not alone. Jesus who had suffered and triumphed was with him. This hidden awareness touched him with a joy so deep that it was reflected on his countenance. His face looked like the face of an angel. The high priest paused in wonder before he spoke.

"Are these things so?" he finally broke the silence.

With the readiness of a man in whom God's Spirit lived, and the boldness of one who knows that truth is on his side, Stephen made his defense.

"Brethren and fathers, hear me," he began with vigorous and passionate voice.

Stephen did not deny the charges made against him. He boldly reaffirmed them before the court that held his life in its hands.

The Holy Land—it was no better than other lands. It was in Mesopotamia, not Palestine, that God spoke to Abraham. It was in Egypt that Joseph became the deliverer of his people. Moses was trained in Egypt. He was called from Midian to deliver his people. The law was given to Moses in the wilderness of Sinai. God was not a God limited to any special land, but the God of the whole universe.

And the Temple? Did not their fathers know God long before the Temple was built? They had only a tent in which to worship in the wilderness. It was sufficient as a religious center. And although the Temple may once have been a fit place to worship God, it had become an idol to the people, a thing of wood and stone which they had substituted for the living God. Had they never read in The Book of Isaiah, that "the Most High dwelleth not in houses made with hands"? No building can contain God. Heaven is his throne. The earth is his footstool. The whole universe cannot contain him, much less a house which human hands have built.

And the law? It too was but an idol to them. They revered it as sacred, but neither their fathers nor they had kept it.

"You stiff-necked people, uncircumcised in heart and ears, you always resist the Holy Spirit. As your fathers did, so do you. Which of the prophets did not your fathers persecute? And they killed those who announced beforehand the coming of the Righteous One, whom you have now betrayed and murdered, you who received the law as delivered by angels and did not keep it."

At this point, the pent-up anger which had been growing as he spoke burst forth. A forest of fists beat the air. Hundreds of feet scraped the marble floor. Those nearest Stephen glared madly into his face, and gnashed their teeth.

"Blasphemer!"

"Traitor!"

"Dog!"

Stephen was like a lamb in a pack of starved wolves, but he was so filled with ecstasy that he seemed blind to the turbulent scene around him. As though in a trance, he saw into the unseen world. He cried out:

"Look! I see heaven open, and Jesus standing on the right hand of God!"

That was enough. Stopping their ears so that they could hear no further blasphemy, at a gesture from the high priest the mob seized Stephen. With raging fury they dragged him out of the judgment hall, through the Temple court, out through the city gate, to stone him.

The witnesses against Stephen were privileged to cast the first stones. They took off their garments and piled them at the

feet of Saul, who was there to witness the outcome of his plot.
The first sharp-edged stone caught Stephen in the face. Blood
began to line his transfigured countenance. He cried,

"Lord Jesus, receive my spirit!"

Then a whole volley of stones, from countless hands in the
crowd, began to crush his body. Falling to his knees, Stephen
called out in his agony,

"Lord, lay not this sin to their charge."

Then he fell asleep.

"Lord, lay not this sin to their charge." . . . "Lord, lay not ·
this sin to their charge." . . . "Lord, lay not this sin to their
charge." . . .

The rest of the scene Saul might have cast from his mind and
gone to sleep. He had but done his duty. He had followed the
demands of his conscience. He had acted for God. But as he
tossed on his pallet that night, he could not rid himself of the
echo of those words: "Lord, lay not this sin to their charge."

What made Stephen say that? How can a man pray for those
who kill him? Was the report true that this Jesus whom he said
he saw standing on the right hand of God died the same way?
What was it reported that he had said? "Father, forgive them;
for they know not what they do." Could it be that the mob did
not know what it had done with Stephen?

And the look on the man's face! How can a blasphemer have
such a heavenly light in his eye? If he really were a bad man,
how could he be so tranquil in death? What made him so sure
that he saw Jesus at God's right hand that he was willing to
commit his spirit to him as his breath expired?

The day lived on into the night.

The face of an angel! . . . The heavens opened! . . . Jesus on
the right hand of God! . . . "Lord Jesus, receive my spirit!" . . .
"Lord, lay not this sin to their charge." . . .

Saul could not sleep.

Captured

HE NEXT MORNING, Saul climbed the narrow, steep streets of Jerusalem to the Temple court. The disturbed thoughts of the night before were quieted.

"How foolish I was," he said to himself, "to have questioned yesterday's action!"

He remembered how, in his boyhood, the coming of daylight showed that the thieves and spirits he feared in the night were but the creaking of the house. His midnight thoughts had no more reality than that, he told himself. There could be no doubt that the man Stephen had blasphemed. He had denied the God of Israel. Inaction would have been treachery. To have listened further to his scandalous doctrine would have been to curse one's self and one's people.

37

So with the coolness of the morning breeze on his face, and the freshness of the rising sun reflected in his eyes, he regained confidence with each step of his ascent.

The sight of the magnificent dome of the Temple sent through him a surge of pride and zeal. Did not that accursed traitor speak against this Temple? Is it not here that God has made his dwelling in the earth? Is it not here that Messiah will suddenly appear? Will not the Capitoline Hill of Rome then give allegiance to this Hill of Zion? Thoughts such as these trampled on each other through Saul's mind. He resolved anew that the earth must be rid of all who held Stephen's views.

As he reached the court of the Temple, he went directly to the stone chamber of the Sanhedrin to discuss the next step to be taken in the light of Stephen's death.

The meeting of the Sanhedrin that morning was unusually short. Lengthy discussion was unnecessary. For weeks they had failed to find a ground for condemning the followers of Jesus on which all parties could agree. Stephen had afforded the point of agreement. His teaching had offended all parties. A systematic plan was, therefore, agreed upon for exterminating all believers in Jesus.

Saul was to take the leadership in suppressing the new doctrine. The misgivings that followed Stephen's execution made him enter upon this new work with vigor. Indecision, he thought, had opened his mind to suggestions from the devil. He would act so decisively that his ears would be shut to the devil's whispers.

Saul threw himself without reserve into a work that normally would have revolted his sensitive nature—brutal work of rounding up men like animals for the slaughter. In the fire of his zeal he behaved like a mad man. Invading every house where Christians were hiding, he had both men and women dragged to prison. Some of the weaker he made to blaspheme. He ordered those who would not give up their faith to be tortured.

Bleeding backs . . . bruised faces . . . frightened women . . . screaming children—Saul did not traffic in these things in normal days. But Saul was another Saul now. The glory of God could not be sacrificed for sentiment. Had not Elijah slaughtered four hundred and fifty prophets of Baal in the name of God? At that time, it was God or Baal. Now it was God or this malefactor Jesus. Saul would be another Elijah. Every follower of Jesus in the city of David he would stamp out at any cost.

But silencing the movement in Jerusalem did not destroy it. That simply spread it. News trickled back to Jerusalem from every city where the persecuted had fled that they were spreading their pernicious doctrines everywhere. Particularly disturbing was word from Damascus. If the Jesus heresy had spread that far, into a Gentile city, there might be no end to it. It must be stifled there too.

So Saul went to the high priest.

"Have you heard?" said he. "This lie about a crucified Messiah has spread to Damascus."

"Yes, God curse its followers, I have heard it."

"Give me letters to the authorities in Damascus, granting me your permission, and I shall drag every son of Belial back to a Jerusalem dungeon. Men or women, they must be ground to the dust," urged Saul.

"But that is beyond my jurisdiction," replied the high priest.

"The Jews recognize your religious authority everywhere," answered Saul. "Your signature is sufficient to command the rulers of the synagogue. And Aretas, the ruler of Damascus, rules by right of Rome. He must keep the peace. He will not dare offend our people in the city. They are rich and influential. Has not Aretas shown his good will by visits to you here in Jerusalem? Your name is all I need. Give me letters, give me men, and every cursed soul who speaks a good word for that Galilaean fool shall be brought to you in chains."

The letters were issued. The men were assigned. The party set out. Impatient, determined, fearless, wrathful, Saul, in command, strode forth to deal the deathblow to this betrayal of his people, this blasphemy against his God.

Damascus was more than 150 miles from Jerusalem. At least five days would be spent on the way. The first miles found the crowd talking loudly, tossing jests back and forth, pointing out historic landmarks, describing the wonders of Damascus, the oldest city in the world. To all this Saul seemed oblivious. His mind dwelt on other things: his letters . . . his mission . . . his victims . . . the vindication of God. Saul seemed to dwell in a world apart from the others.

As the days wore on, weariness and heat turned travel into drudgery. Talking ceased. Spirits dulled. Monotony reigned. Saul had time to think.

His thoughts displeased him. He tried to shut them out. But, barricade his mind as he would, they forced their way in. As he thought of the victims he was going to arrest, faces of those he had bound and beaten in Jerusalem rose up before him. Innocent faces . . . faces with a strange light on them . . . courageous faces . . . faces that smiled forgiveness even when tortured. If only he could forget them!

His own soul's dissatisfaction seemed unbearable. He had given his life to the best he knew. Every ounce of his energy had gone into keeping the law. But he had found no inner peace. He wanted to be a friend of God, but God seemed far off. He was a Judge, who sentenced him for his failures. Saul could only cringe before him as a doomed culprit. And yet, God knew, he had tried. Was this all his religion meant—sheer duty, impossible demands, inner disharmony, moral defeat?

But these Jesus followers—they seemed to have found the secret of life. They had poise, courage, moral victory. All that Saul sought they had found. Could it be that they were right? That would make his whole life a mockery. It would mean that the mission on which he had now embarked was a fool's errand. That could not be.

But the thought would not die.

And that advice of Gamaliel—Gamaliel whom he had loved so deeply as his teacher, Gamaliel against whom he had argued so vigorously because of his tolerance in dealing with the followers of Jesus. What had Gamaliel said about these men he was hunting down? "I tell you, keep away from these men and let them alone; for if this plan or this undertaking is of men, it will fail; but if it is of God, you will not be able to overthrow them. You might even be found opposing God!" Why have these men not given up their cause under persecution? Why is this new teaching, even when condemned, spreading like a contagious disease? Is it possible that it is of God? Can it be that I am fighting God? O God, never! I fight *for* thee!

But the suspicion would not down. To be fighting God when he supposed he was fighting for him—that thought was too much to bear.

And this Jesus—what sort of person was he? Was he a demon-possessed man? an upstart peasant's son who posed as a teacher? a fanatical blasphemer? a despiser of the law? He must have been all these, for Saul's Pharisee friends had told him as much. They must have known, for they had seen and heard Jesus.

But these other stories—how could they have arisen? Men said that he was so kind, so gracious, so humble, so selfless, so radiant. Had the Pharisees made a mistake? Did they kill one sent from God? But he could not have been God's Messiah, or God would not have let him die. Messiah could not be crucified.

Yet his followers say the Jewish Scriptures teach that Messiah must suffer. Nonsense! And yet: "He was despised, and rejected of men." So was Jesus. "A man of sorrows, and acquainted with grief." How like him that sounds! "As a lamb that is led to the slaughter . . . he poured out his soul unto death." There is a strange likeness to Jesus' fate in these words. But the prophet was not speaking of Messiah when he wrote that, was he?

And that man Stephen! . . . That light on his face! "Behold,
I see the heavens opened." . . . "Lord Jesus, receive my spirit."
. . . "Lord, lay not this sin to their charge."

If only he had not died like that!

And that monstrous lie about the resurrection of Jesus—
what if it were not a lie? Nonsense! It *has* to be a lie. But where
did the idea come from? They claim they *saw* him alive after
he was crucified. Absurd! One can't see what doesn't exist. Hallucinations! Imagination! They wished he were alive, and his
living image photographed on their memories seemed real.
That's all. But so many claim they have seen him. Strange,
isn't it? It is not usual for large groups to have identical hallucinations.

And those strange rumors about the empty tomb? Of course
they aren't true. But where is the body of Jesus? Even the
Pharisees admit that it is gone. Where is it? His disciples stole
it, they say. But how could they steal it when the tomb was
sealed and guarded? They seem too honest to have bribed the
soldiers. And would the soldiers have risked the wrath of Pilate
for a bribe, when he had had so much trouble over this whole
affair anyway? Could it be that the leaders of the Pharisees
know otherwise, and created the story of the stolen body? Perhaps that is why Gamaliel hesitated and asked for time to see
how this movement developed?

And to whom was Stephen talking when he died? "Lord
Jesus, receive my spirit." An overwrought imagination, of
course. But why would he imagine that Jesus could receive
his spirit? The last time Stephen had seen Jesus he was a lifeless corpse, who could do nobody any good. Unless . . . unless
he had seen him since, alive! Impossible! My own imagination
is overwrought now. But . . .

Several days of thoughts like these left Saul a shaken man.
At first he told himself that they were caused by overstrain, and
by the enforced lull in his work of persecution. He felt that he
would throw them off when he reached Damascus. The chal-

lenge of the work he was going to do there would lift his spirit out of the gloom. But the darkness enveloped his spirit more heavily as he neared the city.

Suddenly—at midday on the last day of the trip, just as he neared the gate of Damascus—a blaze of light far brighter than the noonday sun struck him to the ground!

He lay there helpless. A voice spoke to him:

"Saul, Saul, why do you persecute me? It hurts you to kick against the goads."

What was happening? Saul hardly knew. Here across his path stood One, invisible yet real, whose presence overwhelmed him with an awe he had never felt before. Shattering power . . . dazzling brilliance . . . Godlike majesty . . . unspeakable mystery . . . strange tenderness! Struck to the ground, yet gently held; crushed, yet loved.

Saul was bewildered. He struggled for speech.

"Who are you?" he gasped.

"I am Jesus, whom you are persecuting."

"I am Jesus!" Then Jesus is alive! "You are persecuting me!" Those words tossed Saul's life in ruins about his feet. The grandest effort of his life was all a mistake! In hounding men for worshiping One whom he thought to be a dead criminal, he was in reality making vicious thrusts at a living Lord. This supreme effort at loyalty to God was supreme disloyalty. Stones hurled at Stephen were stones hurled at the living Jesus! The agony of beaten victims was a hurt in the heart of God's Messiah! Stephen and his friends were right! Saul was wrong! The crucified Jesus was God's Messiah! He was alive! Saul had met him! No evidence could have convinced him before. No evidence could deny it now!

But what should he do? He was too bewildered to know. Of one thing, however, he was certain. He could no longer live at enmity with this One who had overpowered him. He must come to terms with him, and find his place in his will.

So Saul put to him the simple question, "What shall I do?"

"Rise, and enter the city," came the answer. "And you will be told what you are to do."

The companions of Saul stood speechless. They saw their leader struck to the ground by an invisible force. They heard him speak as though he were conversing with someone. But they saw no form and heard no voice. What could it all mean? Filled with fear, they cast anxious glances at each other, and waited.

Shortly, Saul struggled to his feet. He staggered from weakness. He stared glassy-eyed into space.

"Joshua, son of Rechab, give me your hand," Saul finally said to his leading companion.

As Joshua came near and touched Saul's outstretched hand, he heard him say:

"The light! It blinds me! I can see nothing! Lead me to the city."

It was a confused procession that journeyed on into Damascus. The once proud Saul, famed for his learning, stalwart in his leadership, armed with the authority of the high priest to bind and imprison men, came groping into Damascus humbled, broken, blind. His companions were embarrassed at being members of a mission whose leader had so pitifully collapsed. They led him to the house of Judas, in the street called Straight, where Saul was to make his headquarters. After reporting to Judas the strange happenings of their journey's end, they left to hunt up friends of their own or to see the city.

Judas was nonplused. He had planned a gathering of Jewish notables to meet with Saul upon his arrival, to welcome him and to lay plans for the anti-Jesus campaign in Damascus. But here was the famous leader—helpless, seemingly insane, blind. He led Saul to a room, and dispatched servants to cancel the scheduled meeting.

"Here is food for you, Saul," Judas announced shortly, as he returned to Saul's quarters. "Arise and eat."

Saul gave no indication that he heard him.

"Saul, Saul," Judas repeated more loudly. "I have brought you food. It will give you strength. The desert journey was too much for you. Arise and eat, and your health will return."

Saul moved with a start, like one awaking from a dream.

"I do not care for food," he said.

Drink also he refused. He wished only to be let alone.

For three days he seemed to be in a physical coma. He neither ate, drank, nor spoke. All his physical powers were suspended. He lay like a dead man. His pulse and his measured breathing were the only signs of life.

But in his inner life—what activity! Mind, emotions, will, all astir, all vigorously rearranging themselves around a new center. It was as though all his thoughts, feelings, and purposes had suddenly broken loose from their old moorings, and were whirling—whirling like renegade planets through space—toward the pull of a greater gravitation.

Jesus . . . he is alive! . . . As alive as I am. . . . Not monstrous lie, but truth. . . . He isn't in Joseph's tomb. . . . No one stole his body. . . . He walks the road to Damascus! . . . He walks the road to everywhere! . . .

And those scars in his hands . . . deep, but glorious! . . . Why couldn't I see it before? . . . "A man of sorrows, and acquainted with grief." . . . There it was all the time . . . but, God forgive me, I was blind. . . . Through suffering, Messiah entered into his glory!

I—the chief of sinners! . . . I thought I was righteous. I kept the law. No, rather, I tried. I did very well. I exceeded my fellows. I was proud of my achievement. I thought God owed me salvation. . . . But I was God's enemy. . . . I had no greater claim on his mercy than the publicans and the harlots. . . . I stood no whit better with him than the multitude who keep not the law.

How tender his voice was! . . . He could have slain me. . . . I fell before his power as one dead. . . . He knew that I was fighting him. . . . But he spoke my name: "Saul, Saul." . . . No mother ever breathed the name of her sick child half so feelingly. . . . I was persecuting him, yet he loved me! . . . I hated him! I tortured his followers! I made them blaspheme! . . . But he loved me! Me he would forgive! . . .

All men must know this! . . . If the law cannot save, then Jew is no better than Gentile. . . . All need God's mercy. . . . All may have it. . . . I must tell them! . . . I must make amends, O Christ, for my wrongs against you. . . . From henceforth I know but one claim, one passion—the love of Christ! . . . I will bring men to that love with the same passion with which I sought to drive them away from it! . . .

Did I dream? . . . A man named Ananias, the leader of believers here in Damascus, coming to see me? . . . No, that cannot be. . . . He is no doubt hiding from me. . . . But I am not dreaming—I am wide awake. . . . What was that I heard just now?

"I seek Saul of Tarsus. Does he dwell with you?" came a voice from without.

"Three days ago he arrived at my house," replied Judas.

"I am Ananias, son of Jacob. I beg leave to speak with him."

"Speak with him if you can. Some evil spirit has possessed him. He eats not, drinks not, speaks not—dead, for all practical purposes. Since the first few hours I have left him to himself. If you can rouse him, welcome. If you could take him from my house, peace be on you. He is in the room with the red hanging over the door."

Ananias slowly pushed back the heavy hanging. He hesitated momentarily. Then, summoning his courage, he strode across the room to Saul's couch. Pausing for just an instant to breathe a silent prayer toward heaven, he took Saul by the hand.

"Brother Saul," he ventured quietly.

Saul stirred.

"Brother Saul," he repeated, "the Lord Jesus, who appeared to you on the road by which you came, has sent me that you may regain your sight and be filled with the Holy Spirit."

"Brother Saul!" Saul could hardly believe what he heard. He had seen a vision of a man coming in to lay his hands on him and restoring his eyesight. But could it be true? This man, who was high on the list of those whom he had come to drag to prison, called him "Brother." So Jesus' followers did not hate him for all that he had done! They were willing to take him in as a brother!

Immediately Saul's sight returned, and he saw the benign face of Ananias who stood before him.

"Brother Saul," continued Ananias. "I feared to come to see you. I knew how much evil you had done to Jesus' followers in Jerusalem. I knew that you had come here with authority to bind and imprison all who worship him. But the Lord, in a vision, commanded me to come. You are selected by him to be his messenger to all men—Jews and Gentiles, small and great. Arise and come with me."

A surge of strength coursed through Saul's body. He stood on his feet. With the help of Ananias, he took a step.

Judas watched and listened intently. He did not understand what he saw. When Saul took leave of him to go to the home of Ananias, he heaved a sigh of relief. To get this deranged young rabbi off his hands was a stroke of good fortune. He closed the door behind his departing guest with a glad sense of deliverance.

At the home of Ananias, Saul was greeted by a group of friends who had gathered to pray while Ananias visited Saul at the home of Judas. They could hardly believe their eyes when the proud persecutor of whom they had heard so much and whose coming to Damascus they had feared returned with Ananias, meek, subdued, cordial, teachable. To them Saul rehearsed what had happened to him on the road, and told how his thinking about Jesus had been changed by this experience.

"Brother Saul," said Ananias, "baptism is the sign by which we who believe that Jesus is Messiah make public confession of our faith. Are you ready to join with us in this sign?"

"Gladly," replied Saul.

Thereupon a simple service was arranged, and, in the company of other believers, Ananias conducted the rite! His hands trembled a little and his voice quivered with emotion as he said, "I baptize you in the name of Jesus, God's Messiah, who died, and rose, and is coming again."

The tremendous revolution that had overturned Saul's life left him with a strong desire for solitude. He was emotionally and physically exhausted, and needed rest. Furthermore, he wanted to think through the deep meanings of the experience through which he had passed. He took leave of his new friends, therefore, and went into the desert of Arabia, where, away from his former associations and the bustle of life, he could ponder what had happened to him and relate his new-found faith to the Scriptures.

The fact that Jesus was alive convinced him clearly that in him God had completed all that he had been promising throughout the Scriptures—the deliverance of Israel. Still this deliverance was not a mere worldly deliverance from oppressive powers which had overrun the nation. It was a grander thing than that—a deliverance from all moral and spiritual enemies, both in this world and in the unseen world of spiritual forces.

The death of Jesus, then, rather than being a stumbling block, was the glorious point at which Jesus had met man's worst enemy—death—and conquered. The cross was not a symbol of defeat, but the pledge of God's triumph over all evil.

Victory over evil, then, was not the result of human struggling, but the result of what God had done. To be right with God was not a human achievement, but a divine gift. Since it was a gift, it was not to be earned, but simply received. Peace with God comes, not by keeping the law, but by faith in Jesus.

But if salvation is by faith, and not by keeping the law, then a Gentile may be saved as well as a Jew. God's gift is free to all men.

And a gift is given, not because it is deserved, but because of the love of the one who gives it. Salvation is the undeserved gift of a loving God, who has commended his love to us in the death of his Son.

After pondering these and other aspects of his faith for many months, Saul returned to active life to make them known to other men. He went first to Damascus, from whence he had gone into retirement, and began vigorously to announce in the synagogues that Jesus is the Son of God, the hope of Israel, the Redeemer and Lord of all men. His preaching produced great excitement in Damascus.

"Is not this the man who made havoc in Jerusalem of those who believe this doctrine?" men asked.

"Did he not come here some months ago to smash this faith?"

"What has wrought this change in him? How now does he proclaim the teaching he once persecuted to the death?"

Amazement soon gave way to anger. This turncoat must be silenced. His enemies, conniving with the city authorities, laid a plot for his life and guarded every gate of the city to prevent his escape. But Saul's friends outwitted his enemies. Smuggling him late at night to the home of a friend whose house was built on the city wall, they lowered him in a huge basket through a window to the ground, where Saul disappeared into the darkness a free man.

Mingled feelings coursed through his heart as he slipped off into the night. Here were men saving his life—men whom he would gladly have killed but a few months before. But here also were men seeking to kill him, men of whom not so long ago he had been the leader. What a strange reversal of position his experience on the road to Damascus had wrought!

It was to Jerusalem Saul turned when he had to flee from Damascus. He wanted to return to his old headquarters and witness to his new-found faith in the center where his ardent campaign against it had been waged. At first, the Jerusalem church feared him, thinking that his conversion was a pretense through which he could gain information to be used treacherously against them. One of the church leaders, however, named Barnabas, sensed the genuineness of his faith, and persuaded the others to receive him into their fellowship.

His visit to Jerusalem brought Saul in touch with Peter. Peter, who had been with Jesus from the beginning, rehearsed many incidents and teachings of Jesus which Saul was eager to hear. And Saul, as a profound student of the Scriptures, helped Peter to develop the meaning of his faith in Jesus. Momentous were the hours these men spent together—the weather-beaten fisherman of Galilee and the smooth-faced intellectual of Tarsus.

The enmity aroused against Saul in Damascus was soon repeated in Jerusalem. His old friends considered him traitor to their cause, and resolved to kill him. Again he had to flee, this time to his old home, Tarsus. For more than six years Saul lived and worked in Tarsus. But he was not destined to spend his life there. The One who had met him on the way to Damascus was preparing a wider stage of action for him, of which he knew nothing at the moment. A wholly unanticipated turn of events was soon to set him to a task that changed the world.

PART TWO

The Encounter

CHAPTER 4

The Issue

Barnabas!"

"Saul!"

The eyes of the two met. It had been seven years since they had parted, when Saul took ship for Tarsus. For a moment they could not speak. Then Saul broke the silence:

"Where did you come from?"

"From Antioch in Syria," Barnabas replied.

"What brings you here?"

"I have come for you!"

Barnabas then unfolded the chain of events that led him there. A severe dispute, occasioned by an unusual experience of Peter, had been raging in the Jerusalem church. While Peter had been preaching in Joppa, he had a vision. A great sheet was let down from heaven, containing animals that the law forbade Jews to eat. A voice said to him, "Rise, Peter; kill and eat."

Peter refused, insisting that he had never eaten anything forbidden by the law. The voice replied, "What God has cleansed, you must not call common."

Three times this happened. Peter wondered what it could mean. As he pondered the meaning of the vision, three men stood at the gate seeking him. They were two servants and a soldier under the command of a Roman centurion, named Cornelius, who had sent for Peter to come to his home to preach. Although Peter had never entered a Gentile's home before, prompted by the Spirit of God he went.

Amazing, indeed, was the outcome. Peter arrived to find the home of Cornelius filled with relatives and friends. Cornelius related how he had seen an angel in a vision, who had commanded him to send for Peter. He had done so, and they were now gathered to hear Peter's message. While Peter preached to them, the whole company were filled with the Holy Spirit, caught up in an ecstasy, and spoke with strange tongues.

Peter was carried away with what he saw—their eagerness, their ecstasy, their response to his word. He cried out, "Can any man forbid that these Gentiles should be baptized, who have received the Spirit of God as well as we Jews?"

So he baptized them, and stayed with them several days, sharing their fellowship, eating at their tables, instructing them in the Way of Jesus.

When Peter got back to Jerusalem, trouble was in the air.

"You entered the houses of the uncircumcised!" angry voices gibed at him.

"You ate their food! What fellowship have sons of Abraham with Gentiles?"

Peter recounted to them the whole story. He had but entered a door God had opened to him. To refuse would have been to fight against God. Who could protest his action?

This silenced the opposition for the moment, but did not gain a permanent victory. To Peter's opponents, Cornelius was but an exception. He had been a God fearer, friendly to the Jewish faith. He would no doubt be willing to be circumcised, if confronted with the demand, and become a Jewish proselyte. But this exception was by no means to be made the rule. Peter's unheard-of behavior with Cornelius might be overlooked, but it was not to be tolerated as a general practice. Jesus was a Jew. He himself said that salvation was of the Jews. He had not come to destroy the law.

"The Jews are the people of God," they insisted. "If Gentiles wish to come to God, let them first be circumcised and become Jews."

Saul listened eagerly to this recital of events. His face glowed at the story of Cornelius. It darkened at the reaction of the Jerusalem Jews.

"Where do you stand, Brother?" asked Saul pointedly.

"I would open the door for the Gentiles," replied Barnabas. "Did I not confess my views to you in Jerusalem when I vouched for you before Peter and James?"

"I feared you had changed," said Saul. "It is a view hard to hold. It has cost me much."

"And what of Peter?" Saul continued to probe.

"He has wavered."

"Wavered?" rejoined Saul. "Is he a reed shaken by the wind? Admit the Gentiles today—exclude them tomorrow! Was he taught that by his Master, who counted not his life dear for the truth? Truth does not change with the calendar. A yes-no man! He is misnamed 'Rock Man.'"

"Patience, my brother," interrupted Barnabas. "The eagle's first flight is short, then he seeks the shelter of the nest. Peter is nesting now—he will fly again. We must not expect him to move as fast, nor as far, as we in this matter. He is a Jew of Palestine. We grew up among Gentiles—you in Tarsus, I in

Cyprus. There is room in the brotherhood for both him and
us. We must love him, and wait."

"I can have patience, though I confess it is not easy. But surrender—never!" Saul's eyes flashed. "God is not the God of the
Jews only. He is the God of the Gentiles also. Is it not written,
'In the place where it was said . . . , Ye are not my people, there
shall they be called sons of the living God'? Has Peter never
read, 'Whosoever shall call upon the name of the Lord shall be
saved'? There is no distinction between Jew and Greek. The
same Lord is Lord of all."

"You speak the truth, Saul," agreed Barnabas. "I have seen
with my own eyes Gentiles in whom the Spirit of Jesus lives,
who have neither been circumcised nor kept the law. But deep-
rooted prejudice yields slowly. The struggle over this issue will
be long and hard. We must act with wisdom and with patience."

"You are no doubt right, Barnabas. Peter and James and
John are more fettered than we, who grew up outside of Palestine. It may be that we should not be too disturbed about what
the Jerusalem church does, so long as we are free outside Jewish circles to preach to the Gentiles."

"That is just the point of my coming here," replied Barnabas. "The struggle over this question is by no means confined
to Jerusalem. Some of the believers—men of Cyprus and Cy-
rene—who were driven out of Jerusalem during the persecution settled in Antioch of Syria. They have been preaching to
the Gentiles there with marked success. This innovation has
deeply disturbed the Jerusalem church, so that they have appointed me to visit Antioch and investigate the movement. Instead of returning to Jerusalem, I have come to find you, Saul.
The hour has struck. A door has opened to a work in Antioch
for which you are peculiarly fitted. You must enter it."

"Why did you not return to Jerusalem to report?" inquired
Saul. "Do you fear the men of reputation there?"

"Argument is weak, Saul. Argument stirs passions. It deepens prejudices. It breaks fellowship. It hinders work. It is my judgment that the battle will be won not with words, but with deeds. The Gentiles are waiting for our message, and will respond. Let us go to Antioch to kindle a flame of holy fire among the Gentiles, so bright and genuine that no one can stand against it. My report to Jerusalem shall be not in words but in an army of Gentile converts. We will show them that Christ can make true disciples of Gentiles just as well as of Jews. That will convince them. The battle will be ours."

"I am ready," answered Saul.

So the two set out together on their journey. After traveling three days, they arrived at Antioch, which was the third largest city in the Roman Empire. It was an excellent proving ground for testing Saul's views. Jews were there in large numbers. The most famous synagogue outside Palestine, claiming to house some of the holy vessels of Solomon's Temple, added its luster to the many public buildings. Numbers of pagans, weary of their spiritual emptiness, had become converted to the Jewish faith. Some had submitted to all the Jewish rites, others in simpler ways had confessed faith in the God of the Jews, and many of these proselytes were seeking further for truth. Gentiles who were not proselytes had been listening to the message about Jesus. Jew, proselyte, Gentile—could they be fused together in this new movement? Antioch was a good place to make the test.

Did the new message have power to conquer paganism? Antioch would determine that too. Debauchery had reached its lowest level there. It was a center of neither industry nor commerce. It was an administrative city, housing the officials and soldiers who guarded the interests of the Empire in that quarter. To it flocked peddlers, pleasure lovers, office seekers, magicians, prostitutes, stargazers, clowns.

To the natural corruption of such a city was added the depravity of worship connected with the Temple of Apollo. Blood baths, frenzied dances, erotic ritual, all ended in an orgy of unbridled sexual indulgence. The city reeked with the foul smell of disease and the sickening odor of incense and perfumes used to counteract it. Diseased and shameless, men and women lolled in the groves, under the booths, along the porches of the city. If men were ever abandoned to their own depraved desires, it was in Antioch.

Would the pure flame of Saul's gospel burn out this sensual rot, or be smothered by it? Could men and women who had abandoned every good thing, whose spirits had died within them, be quickened by divine love? Could the crown of allegiance be removed from the head of Apollo and placed on the head of One who had once been crowned with thorns? Antioch held the answer.

The work that had been started under others progressed rapidly under the leadership of Saul and Barnabas. The new light began to penetrate the darkness of paganism. The flickering flame kindled by the followers of Christ became a steady blaze. Pagans were converted in such numbers that the movement began to attract public notice. Jew, proselyte, and Gentile were so united that men could no longer think of the new movement as a special brand of Judaism. It became to them a religion in its own right.

A nickname hurled at the members of this fellowship was destined to become famous.

"Christian," called one clown to another.

"Little Christs," a lewd fellow jokingly sneered.

The nickname stuck. The jester who coined it left his mark on every generation since, and on every quarter of the globe where Christians have carried their faith.

For a year Saul and Barnabas saw their work in Antioch grow. In Jerusalem at the same time, however, Christians were enduring hardship. And their suffering and persecution found its origin in the capital of the Roman world, where the emperor Caligula had gone mad. Thinking himself divine, he sought the worship of all men. The Jews alone refused him divine honors. Like a beast foiled of his prey, Caligula roared vengeance.

"Petronius," he shouted, "I send you to Syria to replace Vitellius! If he cannot bring these Jewish dogs to their knees, I command you to do it."

"They are dogs hard to leash," replied Petronius.

"Invade their kennel! Leash them! Choke them!" Caligula raved.

"They differ from other breeds," Petronius risked in protest.

"Dogs are dogs to Romans, whatever their breed!" Caligula shouted.

Petronius tried to remind the emperor of past experience with the Jews. Cyrus had found it wise to favor them. Alexander had pampered them. Antiochus had burned his fingers on them. The Romans had always made concessions to them. They worshiped one God, not many. They were dogs who would bleed, but would not be cowed.

"Curses on their God," railed the emperor. "I am God! If they worship but one God, they will worship me! Begone, Petronius. Take with you a statue of me carved by the imperial sculptors. Set it up inside their holy temple. Let the dogs grovel before me. The Jews shall worship Caligula!"

Petronius, with no enthusiasm, set off on his distasteful task. The Jews, however, by strenuous negotiations led by the high priest, forestalled action by jockeying for time. This, Petronius was glad to give, for he knew how foolish were the orders he had been sent to carry out. Action was delayed again and again, until it seemed impossible to delay it longer, when Caligula was suddenly assassinated and succeeded by Claudius, who was too wise to carry out the plans of his mad predecessor.

Although the Jews thus escaped the tragic consequences of Caligula's folly, there was an outcome to the whole affair which brought suffering upon the Christians in Jerusalem. Herod Agrippa, during the turbulent period in Rome following Caligula's assassination, helped to persuade the senate to accept

Claudius as emperor. Claudius rewarded Herod by adding
Judea and Samaria to his territory. To gain favor with his new
subjects, Herod went out of his way to act like a guardian of
the Jewish faith. Since the Christians seemed to be enemies of
the Jewish faith, Herod courted favor in Jerusalem by persecuting them. He seized James, the son of Zebedee, and be-
headed him. He imprisoned Peter, intending to behead him
also; but Peter escaped from prison by night and fled the city.

During these uncertain days, some leading prophets of the
Jerusalem church fled from Jerusalem and went to Antioch for
safety. After reporting on conditions in the mother church,
one of them, named Agabus, warned that a famine was about
to break. The Jerusalem Christians, already living under the
stress of persecution, in case of famine would suffer even more
severely, for most of them were poor. The Christians in Antioch were more prosperous. This furnished Saul and Barnabas
with an excellent opportunity to vindicate with the Jerusalem
church their policy of admitting Gentiles into the Christian
group, and to bind together the church at Antioch and the
church at Jerusalem. They decided to raise a fund to send relief to their brothers in Jerusalem. Gentile Christians feeding
Jewish Christians during adversity would help to show that
they were one in Christ. When men suffer together, they are
less likely to quarrel over differences of custom and practice.

A generous relief fund was immediately raised, and Saul
and Barnabas were dispatched with it to Jerusalem. How this
gift raised the spirits of the brothers there! They were not
alone in their suffering, but were a part of a larger fellowship
in which the strong bore the burdens of the weak. And the
question of Gentiles being admitted into the Christian church
at Antioch—well, who could deny their right to belong to the
fellowship when they had vindicated their genuine faith by
sacrificial benevolence? Deeds spoke louder than arguments.
Food for those who were starving, sympathy for those who were
being persecuted—these things overshadowed differences of

judgment. No question was raised about the Antioch situation, and Saul and Barnabas felt that circumstances had combined to relieve the tension that might otherwise have prevailed.

When their mission of mercy was ended, it was three men, not two, who set their faces toward the port to sail for Antioch. John Mark, a young cousin of Barnabas, had joined them. He was from a leading family who, after attaining great wealth in the island of Cyprus, had returned to Jerusalem to live. His widowed mother had opened her large home to the Christians in Jerusalem. Peter, James, John, Barnabas, and other Christian leaders made this home their headquarters. Frequent meetings of the believers were held there too.

Hence, Mark had become well versed in Christian teaching through his intimate fellowship with the apostles. Prior to his conversion he had been a minister in the synagogue, which had given him experience in teaching. It was natural, therefore, that Barnabas should request him to accompany him and Saul on their return to Antioch. His youth, his ability, his experience, his knowledge, his kinship with Barnabas, all made him a worthy helper in the work that these two great leaders had set for themselves. With high enthusiasm, the trio set their faces toward the north.

Momentous events were in the making at Antioch. The conversion of many leading Gentiles to the Christian faith gave the church an abundance of leadership. Symeon, Lucius, Manaen the foster brother of Herod—all these were teachers and prophets of great ability. The presence of Barnabas and Saul was no longer necessary. The conviction grew that what had happened in Antioch could happen in other Greek centers.

As they worked and worshiped and prayed, the whole group felt that God wanted them to send Barnabas and Saul to preach in other cities. The two men had often spoken of carrying the light into a wider circle. Ever since Saul saw the great light on the road to Damascus, he had known that that light was for all men. Now that the church at Antioch was rooted deeply enough so that no storm could uproot it, and relations between the churches of Antioch and Jerusalem seemed to be cordial, they felt that the hour had come to move out into the Greek world.

The whole church knew how important this move was. They therefore gathered for prayer to inaugurate the new venture with fervent entreaty for God's blessing. So intense was their prayer that for a time they took no food.

"God has sent us a light to lighten the Gentiles," said Symeon. "We must send them the Light of the World."

The group finally gathered solemnly to consecrate Saul and Barnabas for their mission. With these two in the center, the others circled around them and laid their hands on them. Lucius led the prayer.

"O Lord, thou that didst make the heaven and the earth and the sea, and all that in them is," he began. An audible surge of united devotion lifted heavenward.

"Grant unto these thy servants grace to speak the word with all boldness," he continued. "Lay bare thy holy arm in the eyes of all the nations, that all the ends of the earth may see the salvation of our God."

Long and tender were the parting words following the service of prayer. At last Saul and Barnabas broke away from the group, taking John Mark with them, and made their way to Seleucia, the seaport of Antioch.

CHAPTER 5

The Strategy

"CAN WE SAIL directly to Cyprus?" Saul asked.

"The gods favor it," the captain replied. "They often breathe from the west at this time of year. When that happens, it's hug the coast and sail when you can. But today we head for open sea. The wind-gods must be drunk. They breathe heavily from the east."

"There is but one God," Saul spoke almost instinctively.

"Must I listen to that prattle again?" sneered the captain. "I might have known from your looks you were a Jew. Good it is that the winds blow right. We shall reach Salamis soon, and dump our Jewish cargo."

Saul, Barnabas, and Mark were warmly welcomed in Cyprus.

"Son of Consolation!" cried an old neighbor of Barnabas. "You have come home at last! Do you think so little of your friends to stay away so long?"

The eagerness with which Barnabas was greeted on every hand satisfied Saul that Cyprus was a good place to begin their work. The respect in which his companion was held would give them a ready hearing among the Jews. Furthermore, some who fled Jerusalem at the death of Stephen had come to Cyprus. The new teaching, therefore, was not strange. It was already rooted in the island.

In the course of a few weeks, Barnabas and Saul and John Mark, following the main roads of the island, had visited several of the leading cities en route to Paphos, the capital, at the western end. There they taught both in the synagogues and in the open air. The enthusiasm and conviction with which they spoke commanded their listeners, and what they had to say produced widespread interest.

A knock at their door surprised them one evening as they talked over the events of the day.

"Are you the strangers who taught in the market place today?" asked the caller.

"We persuade men daily," replied Saul.

"I bear you an invitation from Sergius Paulus, the proconsul. He desires to hear you."

"We will go gladly," answered Saul.

"He bids you come to the palace at midmorning tomorrow," stated the messenger. "I will call for you."

"The hour will find us ready," Saul promised. "Bear to the proconsul our greetings and good will."

Saul closed the door as the messenger disappeared in the darkness.

What could the proconsul want? Had complaint been made to him by enemies? Were they being summoned to trial?

John Mark feared so.

Or had the proconsul heard something of their teaching and desired to learn more?

Saul and Barnabas hoped so.

But if their hopes were right, why was he interested? Was he merely curious? Or might it be that this was their first opportunity to win a Gentile convert among Roman officialdom?

After long discussion they decided to commit the whole matter to God in prayer and await developments.

"Lord God of Israel," they prayed, "who dost not fear the raging of the heathen, and who reignest over the judges of the earth, reveal thy power to this ruler. Stay him from violence. Instruct him in the way of righteousness. Give to us wisdom and courage. Our times are in thy hand. We commit to thee the morrow and its needs."

John Mark slept lightly from fear. Saul slept lightly from excitement.

"A light to lighten the Gentiles.". . . "The people that

walked in darkness have seen a great light.". . . "The earth shall
be filled with the knowledge of the glory of Jehovah, as the
waters cover the sea.". . . A Roman proconsul become a Christian, Christ invading the ranks of Caesar . . . the kingdoms of
this world become the Kingdom of our Lord.

On such thoughts as these Saul finally lulled himself to light
sleep. The morrow was to be a momentous day.

The three men arose early in the morning. They took no
breakfast, but gave themselves to prayer. John Mark recalled
words of Jesus he had heard Peter rehearse: "Before governors
and kings shall ye be brought for my sake, for a testimony to
them and to the Gentiles."

But what should they do and what should they say when
they came before the proconsul? Other words of Jesus brought
them reassurance:

"When they deliver you up, do not be anxious how you are
to speak or what you are to say; for what you are to say will be
given to you in that hour; for it is not you who speak, but the
Spirit of your Father speaking through you."

"Father, fill us with thy Spirit," they prayed, "that our words
may be thy word to the proconsul."

As they sat brooding over what awaited them, the messenger
arrived. Through the narrow streets of Paphos he led them,
out of the humbler quarter of the city, where they lodged,
toward the suburb where the proconsul had his palace. Long
lines of trees, interspersed with flowering shrubs and vines,
lined the approaches to the palace. Through columned gates
they strode, past formal gardens dotted with marble pavilions,
by sparkling fountains, over arched bridges. At intervals they
encountered guards who, recognizing the messenger of the
proconsul, bowed their assent as they passed.

They faced Sergius Paulus in a large hall lined with costly
wood and ivory and surrounded by stately statues. He lay half
reclining on a large divan, fanned by a dark-skinned slave.
Around him stood a group of court followers—personal

friends, young Romans preparing for future administrative positions, official attendants, men of learning and art whom the proconsul found agreeable to him.

Saul and Barnabas and John Mark stood quietly just inside the door. The messenger walked forward to the proconsul and bowed.

"The men you sent for, Your Excellency," he said.

Sergius Paulus dismissed him with a nod.

"Come near," he beckoned with a wave of the hand to the three visitors.

"Who are you? Whence do you come?" the proconsul questioned.

"Your Excellency," answered Saul for the group, "I am Paul, a freeborn Roman from Tarsus. This is Barnabas, a native of this island, and John Mark, of Jerusalem. We are but lately come from Antioch in Syria."

This was the first time that Saul had used his non-Jewish name, Paul. But he was addressing a Roman, speaking, not as a Jew to a Gentile, but as a man to a man. To the Gentiles he would become a Gentile. From henceforth he was to be known as Paul.

"I am told that you are philosophers, who discourse on the nature of God and of man," said Sergius Paulus. "I desire to know your thoughts."

"We are not philosophers, excellent sir," replied Paul. "We are bearers of good news from God. Philosophers speak the wisdom of this world. But the wisdom of this world is foolishness with God. We speak God's wisdom."

"I have known much of philosophy," continued the proconsul, "but have not known peace."

"The world through its wisdom has failed to know God," replied Paul. "But it was God's good pleasure through the simple truth of what we preach to make himself known to all who would believe it."

"Set forth your preaching to me," asked Sergius.

"God is a God of righteousness," began Paul, "and no evil can stand in his presence. All men, both Jews and Greeks, have done evil. All men, therefore, are condemned before God. But God loves all men, and he sent to this world his Son, Jesus, in whose name we preach. This Jesus sinful men crucified and killed; but God raised him up from the dead. And today he lives and reigns at the right hand of God. Our good news is that he died for our sakes, and all who believe on him are forgiven and through faith in his resurrection granted life everlasting."

"Listen no further!" interrupted a husky, penetrating voice. "God cannot become man. This Jesus about whom he speaks was a criminal crucified by Pontius Pilate. Worship an ass, O Sergius, rather than listen to this worthless palaver!"

The speaker was a Jewish magician, Bar-Jesus by name, who claimed to be able to read the secrets of nature. Religion and science combined gave him a hold on the mind of Sergius Paulus and a place at court. He saw in Paul and his friends the champions of a rival religion which, if the proconsul believed, would undermine his own position.

Paul had sensed a deep response to his word in Sergius Paulus. His high hopes of the night before, that he might see a Roman official converted to Christ, seemed near realization. Would this impostor interpose and stop the work of God?

A rush of divine power came over Paul. Something of that overpowering energy that had thrown him to the ground on the Damascus road seemed to fill him for the moment. He turned blazing eyes on Bar-Jesus—eyes that had looked on divine glory and therefore knew no fear of man, eyes that could penetrate like a rapier.

"Villainous rascal! Son of the devil! Enemy of all righteousness!" cried Paul. "Will you not cease to pervert the right ways of the Lord?"

Bar-Jesus slunk back, trembling. Sergius Paulus looked on in astonishment.

"Behold, the hand of the Lord is upon you," Paul continued. "You will be blind, unable to see the sun for a time."

A haze began to fall over Bar-Jesus' eyes. Pale, shaking, distraught, he tried to leave the hall. He groped. He faltered.

"I cannot see," he whined. "Will someone help me?"

A court attendant took him by the hand and led him away.

As Paul returned to his lodging at the close of the day—for he reasoned with Sergius until nightfall—two convictions were confirmed in his soul. First, the gospel could conquer the world. He would carry it to the ends of the earth. Furthermore, the gospel was for *all* men. In Christ, there was neither Jew nor Greek. Sergius Paulus was proof of that. Paul would work through the Jews where he could, for their schooling in the Scriptures provided solid material on which to build the Church among those who believed. But he would work through them for the salvation of the Gentiles as well. Freedom of access to God through Christ for all men he would champion at any cost.

The tour of Cyprus was completed. Success had justified their efforts. Now they must push farther. So the three travelers boarded a boat which set its course toward Perga in Pamphylia.

Perga—could Paul ever forget it! Wearied from his strenuous tour of Cyprus, nervously keyed up by his efforts with Sergius Paulus, depressed by the discomforts of his sea voyage, he was struck down by malaria. Raging fever, unquenchable thirst, chills which made him shake like a leaf, headache which felt like red-hot steel thrust into his forehead—these left Paul pitifully helpless.

What should he do? To stay in Perga was impossible. To return home was to abandon their work. It was possible that relief could be found by moving to the mountains, where the bracing climate might restore Paul to health. But the trip—how could it be made?

John Mark was for returning. Paul, with his iron will, was for trying the trip up the mountains to Pisidian Antioch. Barnabas was caught between the ties of kinship which bound him to his cousin and the loyalty which he bore to Paul.

"I will recover in Antioch," urged Paul. "We can preach there as well as here. The work must go on."

"Antioch!" mourned John Mark. "Your fever has blurred your reason, Paul. How will you get to Antioch? How could you drag your shaking body a hundred miles over the tortuous mountain trail to Antioch? Can you climb passes too steep for a well man? And how, in your condition, would you swim two rivers? How would you defend yourself from the wild beasts that roam those mountains? And the passes are robber-infested. You might recover in Antioch, yes. But you will never see Antioch alive! Antioch in Syria is the place where you should head, or Jerusalem, not Antioch in Pisidia. Boats leave weekly. I have already made inquiry. We can sail to safety and health at sunup tomorrow."

Paul let the younger man have his say. He was too weak and miserable to argue.

"Have you not yourself," Paul asked, "told us the words of Jesus: 'No man, having put his hand to the plow, and looking back, is fit for the Kingdom of God'?"

"But when the blade is broken, it is useless to plow with the beam," answered Mark.

"The blade is not broken, Mark. It is but momentarily dulled. It will be resharpened in Antioch. We shall plow again," said Paul.

"If you go toward Antioch, you will go without my company." Mark spoke firmly. "And when the news of your death comes to Jerusalem, I will tell them that I am innocent of your blood. And your enemies will say that the foolhardiness that led you to your death was the same that led you to the Gentiles."

"We go to Antioch," insisted Paul. "If you will come with

us, well. If not, farewell. This is no expedition for weaklings. I need men of sterner stuff!"

At sunup the next morning, Mark, standing on the deck of a sloop headed for Jaffa, took his last look at Perga. At the same hour, two men set their faces northward toward the mountain passes. One dragged himself along by sheer will power and the life of his spirit which mastered his broken body; the other gave him what support he could, and prayed that death might not take his companion from him.

How the two ever made the trip none but God will ever know. But a week later Paul lay in the shade beside a hut in Pisidian Antioch. Delirious with head pains and chills, he was watched by an interested group who had never seen a man shake as he did. The bracing air of Antioch, however, began to do its work, and within a few weeks Paul had sufficiently recovered to begin moving about among the friends whom Barnabas had already made.

The kindness the men of Antioch showed to Paul was beyond anything he had ever experienced. There were devout men among them who seemed to have been waiting for the message Paul brought. An angel from heaven would have been given no better reception. If possible, Paul's friends would have plucked out their eyes for him.

The first Sabbath Paul was able to attend the synagogue service, the ruler of the synagogue asked him to speak. The Scripture lessons for the morning gave him his theme. The reader had read the law from the book of Deuteronomy: "Jehovah thy God bare thee, as a man doth bear his son. . . . But ye rebelled against the commandment of Jehovah."

The passage from the prophets carried the same theme. It was the word of God through Isaiah: "I have nourished and brought up children, and they have rebelled against me."

The love of God, tender as a father . . . the rebellion of man, stubborn as an animal—this was Paul's theme, drawn from these Scriptures.

He spoke fervently, recalling God's love shown in their history, against which their fathers had rebelled. He proclaimed God's love in sending his Son, whom the men of Jerusalem had killed. Now God's mercy was shown to them in offering them forgiveness of sins through Jesus, a forgiveness that they had not found in the law.

"Beware, therefore," he exhorted, "lest you reject God's love, and there come upon you what the prophets spoke of, 'Behold, you despisers, and wonder, and perish'!"

The effect was instant. Crowds followed them to their lodging to hear more. Paul and Barnabas were invited to speak again the following Sabbath.

The Sabbath came. The synagogue was crowded out. It seemed as though the whole city had gathered to hear Paul. But the leaders of the Jews had a change of mind. The flocking of the Gentiles to Paul's message offended them. Paul's insistence that the law had failed, and that redemption was God's gift through Jesus, offended them. Some of the bolder ones began to contradict Paul as he spoke. Others joined in. Soon the place was in a hubbub of confusion. Finally, Paul spoke out against them boldly.

"It was necessary that the word of God should first be spoken to you Jews," he cried. "But seeing you thrust it from you, and thus show yourselves unworthy of eternal life, we leave you and turn to the Gentiles."

Paul and Barnabas then went out from the synagogue, and spoke in the open to the Gentiles. Many believed their word, and a great stir went out through the city.

The Jews, however, used their influence with the wealthy and influential leaders of the city to stir up trouble. Fearing a riot between Jews and Gentiles, the city fathers sent officers to command Paul and Barnabas to leave the city. With threats and blows, they were cast out of the city in which they had received such a warm welcome only a few weeks before.

But the trip to Antioch in Pisidia had been justified. Paul's health had been regained, and many in Antioch had believed in Jesus.

The travelers made their way southeastward along the main road which crossed Asia Minor to the next town of importance, Iconium. The experience at Antioch was repeated here. Both Jews and Greeks received them gladly at first. Then hostile Jews stirred up trouble. Paul and Barnabas stood their ground, however, carrying on their work in spite of the hostility they encountered.

Finally a plot was laid to stone them. News of it reached their ears.

"We must flee, Paul," counseled Barnabas.

"Flee?" answered Paul. "You speak like John Mark! Did our Lord flee when they plotted for his life? Was Stephen terrified? Did he run when his life was at stake? The death of Stephen opened my eyes. My death may open theirs. I stay."

"Your courage outruns your judgment, Paul," Barnabas replied. "You have forgotten that our Lord did not run into the jaws of death the first time they plotted against his life. Several times he escaped. 'My time is not yet come,' he said. It is well to die when God wills. It is suicide to die by our will. Your hour is not come. God needs you. This work will perish without you. You must root this plant deeper before you leave it, if you expect its fragrance to girdle the earth and its leaves to be for the healing of the nations."

Paul was convinced. That night they fled. It went hard with Paul to run like a fugitive, to sneak down back lanes, to hide in shrubbery until the sound of feet had passed, to crawl stealthily out the city gate while a friend, by prearrangement, engaged the sentry in conversation. He knew that men would call him coward. They would say that he talked courageously but wilted at the test. Yet, urged on by Barnabas, he knew that he must bear even this for Jesus' sake. The promptings of his own proud nature he must deny, the false accusations of petty men he must endure, that he might win the Roman world for Christ.

The town of Lystra lay next in their path. Since it was not a commercial center, Lystra had few Jews and no synagogue. Paul and Barnabas found shelter, however, in the home of a Jewish widow named Eunice, who had married a Greek. Her son Timothy, because of the father's influence, had not been circumcised. Yet Eunice, and her own mother, Lois, had remained devoutly true to the Jewish faith. Although Timothy was but a lad, the visit of Paul to his home left such a mark on him that he later became one of Paul's most trusted companions and helpers.

The apostles sought opportunity to preach to the inhabitants of Lystra in the market place. Seated before them, listening intently to their word, was a cripple who had never walked. Sensing that he was a man of faith, and being deeply touched by his plight, Paul stood before him, and called out,

"Stand upright on your feet!"

The spiritual force of the one who spoke united with the spiritual eagerness of the one who heard. Like a flash, the man felt that he could command those helpless limbs which had never walked. He leaped to his feet. His face flushed with excitement. His arms stretched out for balance. Slowly he began to walk around.

The effect of this on the multitude in the market place was electric. A thousand times in childhood they had heard the legend of the gods Zeus and Hermes visiting in the guise of needy strangers. Repulsed at door after door, the story went, they finally found an old peasant couple who took them in and received their blessing. The people of Lystra felt that the old story was being re-enacted for them now. So in their native tongue, which Paul and Barnabas did not understand, they began to cry out:

"The gods are come down to us in the likeness of men! Zeus and Hermes walk our streets once more!"

The mighty roar of the crowd slowly faded in the distance as the multitude moved off and left Paul and Barnabas standing alone with the man who had been made to walk. But as they conversed with him about the faith, again they heard the thunder of human voices. Nearer and nearer it came. A saffron-robed priest led the surging mob. Behind him several oxen, garlanded with flowers, were goaded on. Temple girls danced. Flutes and drums set up a weird music.

"What does this mean?" Paul asked his new friend.

"The priest of Zeus comes to sacrifice," he replied. "They think your friend is Zeus and you are Hermes."

Paul grasped his hair in both hands. He looked desperately at Barnabas, wondering for the moment what they should do. Suddenly, with an instinct prompted by no words, both men rushed forward before the crowd, tearing their garments in long shreds in protest.

"Stop!" they cried.

Then, shouting as loudly as he could in order to be heard above the din of the crowd, Paul called out:

"We are not gods! We are but men of like nature with you! We bring you good news from the living God. Put away these follies. Turn to the true God, who made heaven and earth and the sea and all that in them is. It is he that hath given you all good things. To him alone you owe homage. We have come to tell you of him. In time past he allowed each nation to serve its own gods. But now, through Jesus Christ, he is making himself known to you. Put away your idols, and turn to him in faith!"

Scarcely could Paul and Barnabas persuade them to desist. Little by little, looking at each other in amazement and in disappointment, the crowd began to disperse, and the priest and his attendants returned to the temple outside the city gates. It was a great disappointment for them. They thought they had seen gods, but they found they were but men. They had expected more marvels, but they heard only the moral demands of repentance and belief in an unseen God of whom they had never heard.

Disappointed enthusiasm turns quickly into hostility. When, shortly, Jews from Antioch and Iconium pursued Paul and Barnabas to Lystra and denounced them publicly as liars and frauds, the crowds, in their disappointment, turned on them like wounded animals. Enraged, they grabbed up stones and hurled them at Paul. Several of them struck him viciously. One rock, well aimed, caught him on the head. His knees buckled. His eyes slowly closed. His face became pale as death. He lay lifeless on the ground. Friends, acting quickly, had whisked Barnabas away from the center of the mob and saved him from a similar fate.

The collapse of Paul satisfied the fury of the mob. Thinking him to be dead, they dragged him out of the city and cast him in a heap beside the road, where his friends stood over him grieving.

Suddenly his eyes opened. He looked up, like a man awakened from a dream, at the eager faces above him. Where was he? . . . It all came back in a flash. He smiled. He seemed to hear words ringing in his ears: "Blessed are ye when men shall persecute you for my sake. Rejoice, and be exceeding glad." How often had John Mark repeated to him those words of Jesus!

A dozen friends reached quickly when Paul raised his arm for help. He struggled to his feet. On the shoulders of men who would have died for him, he was supported back into town to his lodging and to rest.

The next morning, bruised and limping, Paul set out with Barnabas for Derbe. It was on the frontier of the Roman province of Galatia. Here they stayed for several weeks. Enemies did not pursue them here, so they had peace. Many converts to the Christian faith were made. The encouragement of success and freedom from persecution brought renewal of both body and spirit to the two apostles.

Their decision as to the next move was a difficult one. They could have gone on eastward by the main road which passed through the Cilician Gates to Tarsus, and from thence back to Antioch. Safety dictated this course. But what of the little churches they had founded in the cities they had but lately visited? If these were to survive, they needed encouragement, organization, and instruction. It was dangerous to return, however. At Antioch, Paul and Barnabas had been officially cast out of the city. At Iconium they had had to flee for their lives. At Lystra Paul had been stoned. To return to any one of these places was a risky venture.

But they went back. Each city was visited in turn. Officers were appointed in the churches. Plans were laid for the churches to witness to others. Instruction was given in the deeper things of the faith. Through prayer, fasting, and fellowship the little Christian groups were knit together into solid, compact units, prepared to survive hardship and to propagate their new-found faith among other men.

As they reached the sea and boarded ship for Antioch, Paul thought of John Mark's departure several months before. He had returned to Jerusalem to await word of Paul's death. But Paul was very much alive. And, what was more, several living churches had been born in the cities of Galatia. The gospel had taken root in the Roman world in a fashion to convince Paul that one day it would spread to the ends of the earth.

On their return to Antioch, the church gathered to hear the travelers tell of their trip. The venture on which they had been sent had been successful beyond their hopes. The door of faith had been opened to the Gentiles. Christianity was no longer a Jewish sect; it was a faith for all men. There was great joy in Antioch.

CHAPTER 6

The Clash

EVER SINCE John Mark had arrived back in Jerusalem, the work of Paul and Barnabas had been brought under increasing suspicion by the Jewish Christians there. Mark's report of his experiences reopened the old question raised by Peter's visit to the home of Cornelius. Peter's opponents stirred again.

"Just as I told you," growled an old Christian Pharisee. "I knew Peter was wrong at the time. Let in the camel's nose and he'll take the whole tent!"

"If they had listened to me," complained another, "this Gentile compromise would have been stopped with the Cornelius affair. To let down the bars for one is to let them down for all."

"Why should the way be made easy for Gentiles?" a third argued. "Circumcision has always been the sign of God's covenant with his people. If the Gentiles believe in the God of Israel and accept his Messiah, let them bear witness boldly by accepting the ancient sign."

Bitterness deepened because the mission of Paul and Barnabas had been inaugurated without consulting the Jerusalem church. Why should the young church at Antioch launch questionable ventures without the consent of the mother church? Jerusalem was the home of Judaism and the cradle of Christianity. To her belonged Jesus and the apostles. Authority to carry forward Christ's mission had been vested there. Had the Antioch church sought counsel of the leaders in Jerusalem, this unfortunate compromise with the Gentiles might have been avoided.

Greater heat was generated when Mark reported that Paul was taking over the leadership from Barnabas. Who was Paul to work independently of James and Peter and John? Barnabas had at least been sent out from the Jerusalem church. Even though he may have overstepped the bounds of his commission in going to the Gentiles, his commission had been given originally by the apostles. But Paul? He was not one of the twelve apostles. Nor had he been in on the movement at the beginning. Neither had he been commissioned by the Jerusalem church to do what he had done. To permit the leadership of this fanatical innovator to go unchallenged might be the death-blow to the true faith.

Peter sought to quiet these rumblings, but without success. Behind his back, bitter comments laid at his door the blame for all the discontent. His treatment of Cornelius had set the precedent for Paul. Paul was merely carrying Peter's action to a logical conclusion.

What could be done? Several of the most embittered decided secretly to send persuasive men to Antioch to challenge the church there. They would invade Paul's lair, and beard the lion in his own den. So, under the guise of a friendly visit to their brethren, they set out.

The unexpected arrival of these men in Antioch was hailed with gladness by the Christians there. The believers in Antioch knew what the church at Jerusalem meant to them—it had nurtured the faith of those who first brought them the gospel; it was the center of the life and work of Jesus in whom they believed. Earlier visitors from Jerusalem, such as Agabus, had brought them encouragement and counsel. So they eagerly welcomed these new friends, and invited them to speak at their service of worship.

"Brethren, peace be with you," began the leading speaker. "News of your work has come to us in Jerusalem. It has been reported that many Gentiles have attached themselves to the church here. Our eyes bear witness to the truth of that in this gathering. It is well that this should be. For salvation is of the Jews. The prophets spoke of the isles waiting for the law of the Lord, and the nations coming up to the mountain of his house to be taught of him.

"But enthusiasm often leads to error. It is rumored that Gentiles have been admitted to the fellowship of God's people without meeting the requirements of admission laid down in the law. If this be true, their religion is vain. Men cannot lay aside the commands of God. To you Gentiles who have not met the demands of the law, we must bring warning with all firmness: Unless you are circumcised according to the custom of Moses, you cannot be saved."

As the speaker continued, Paul's heart sank. He and Barnabas had hoped that the success of their work among the Gentiles would conquer such narrowness. Surely, they had thought, the evidence of the Spirit of Christ living in men would prove them Christians, in spite of deep-rooted tradition which demanded circumcision. Dejectedly they sensed that their hopes were not realized. Apparently this issue was not one that could be settled by time and patience. They had tried to let sleeping dogs lie in the hope that they would never awaken. Yet here they were, awake and vicious! It was clear that the issue would have to be brought out into the open. A decisive battle would have to be fought if the Gentiles were to be freed forever from the demands of the Jewish law.

Paul was not one to shirk a fight. He did not relish it, but if the lines had to be drawn and a position defended, he was ready. The cause was great enough to justify a stand. Either the faith must be freed from the bonds of Jewish custom or it would degenerate into a mere Jewish sect—and die! The release from dead tradition and the power of a new life which had come to Paul and countless converts could win the whole world if set free. Paul dreamed of a day when men of every nation and tongue would worship Christ as Lord. But if they had first to become Jews, his dreams were in vain.

Paul and Barnabas had little difficulty in challenging the views of these visitors from Jerusalem to the satisfaction of the church in Antioch. But the issue was larger than that. It would have to be faced openly with the mother church in Jerusalem. Paul had no question about the truth of his gospel. But if his work among the Gentiles was to be permanent, an official agreement with the Jerusalem leaders would have to be reached, whereby the efforts of such men as those who had sought to disrupt the work in Antioch would be discredited. The question must be settled once and for all. The way must forever be opened for all men to believe in Christ without keeping the Jewish law. The law had never brought spiritual life even to the Jews. It was merely a prod to their conscience, showing them that they were sinners in need of salvation. But the law never brought salvation. Paul had tested it to the limit and found it vain. Christ had done what the law could never do—brought forgiveness and a new quality of life. Since he came, the law was not a help but a hindrance. It must not be a requirement for salvation. And this must be said openly, fearlessly, and finally.

Paul determined therefore to go to Jerusalem to force the issue. Barnabas concurred in his judgment, as did the entire Antioch church. It was decided that both Paul and Barnabas should make the trip, accompanied by several other believers from Antioch. On his own initiative, Paul took with him a Gentile named Titus, a young man to whom he had become deeply attached.

The journey was launched by a gathering of the entire congregation for prayer. As the service concluded, the whole group accompanied their emissaries outside the city gates and a mile or two along the road toward Jerusalem. There the larger group reluctantly turned back to Antioch, sensing the weightiness of the mission on which the others were going, and wishing that they could accompany them all the way.

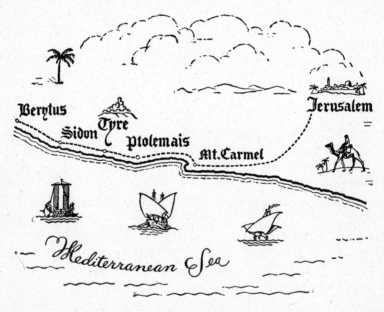

The road lay along the Mediterranean coast, passing through Berytus, Sidon, Tyre, and Ptolemais. Where Mount Carmel juts out into the sea, the travelers turned inland along the way that led through many Samaritan villages to Jerusalem.

In many of the towns through which they passed there were little Christian groups, to whom the story of the work in Antioch and the missionary journey of Paul and Barnabas brought great joy. During the three weeks of the journey, night after night found the travelers sitting up until late hours, their hosts unwilling to miss anything that could be learned in one short visit. Without exception, news of the Gentiles' acceptance of the gospel brought great joy to those who heard it. This gladdened Paul's heart. But what would the church in Jerusalem think? That was the crucial question, on the answer to which so much depended.

On their arrival, Paul and his group found a warm welcome among the Christians in Jerusalem. Whatever their differences of opinion, the bonds that united believers in Jesus were strong; and the coming of visitors to report on the Church's progress in distant places was an occasion for rejoicing. Especially was this true now because of the affection in which Barnabas was held by his Jerusalem friends. A great crowd came together to greet them, including not only the apostles and elders, but also many other members of the church.

Paul and Barnabas rehearsed the victories of the gospel over paganism, both in Antioch and at the places they had visited on their tour of Cyprus and Asia Minor. The story made good telling, and for a long time held the crowd enthralled. They studiously avoided raising the question about circumcision, fearing that it would be folly to discuss the matter openly before the entire crowd. Some zealot would be sure to set off a general uproar by making an extreme or unguarded statement. This would arouse the emotions of the less thoughtful, and create a scene from which no good could come. Paul hoped to face this issue first in private with the leaders. He felt that if he could meet with them alone, he could convince them of the rightness of his cause. Then in public meeting these men of influence would throw their weight on his side and bring the issue to a successful conclusion.

All went well until late in the evening, when a dour-looking old Pharisee believer, who had been unimpressed by Paul's story, spoke up.

"Brother Saul," he called out, for he would not address him by his Gentile name, "the revelation of God is without error. The Lord does not change, nor do his demands. He has given us a law. Have you not read what Moses said: 'O Israel, hearken unto the statutes and unto the ordinances, which I teach you, to do them; that ye may live. Ye shall not add unto the word which I command you, neither shall ye diminish from it'? God is not a man that he should change his mind. The law is eternal. If these Gentiles believe in Messiah, they must be circumcised and keep the whole law of Moses."

A wave of whispering swept the entire group, and soon broke into a roar of discussion. Nothing that Paul could have planned would have done his cause so much good as the old man's statement. The Pharisees who had become believers were still as insistent upon the duty of keeping every jot and tittle of the law as they had been in the days before they believed. The rest of the Christians, on the other hand, kept the law as it was popularly observed by the non-Pharisaic Jews. They were circumcised, they observed the Sabbath, they kept the feasts, they followed in a general way the major requirements of the law; but they did not adhere strictly to all the rigorous demands that Pharisaic tradition had developed. They admired the Pharisees who did, but they felt unable to burden themselves with such demands.

The crowd might have agreed with the Pharisee who had spoken had he merely demanded that the Gentiles be circumcised. But when he went beyond that and insisted that they be required to keep what the Pharisees regarded as the whole law, he was really interjecting another question. If the Gentiles had to keep every Pharisaic rule and regulation in order to be Christians, so would the Jews. In what the old man had said, therefore, he was laying a burden not only on the converts from paganism, but also on the Jewish Christians who were not of the Pharisaic party.

This turn of events was startling. It moved attention away from Paul's problem to a broader problem which affected every man present. But the hour was late, and this new issue must be thought through thoroughly before any final decision about it could be made. The group therefore disbanded to meet on a later occasion.

Paul and Barnabas arranged a private meeting, at the home of John Mark's mother, with Peter, James, and John, and a few of the leading elders. They could speak more frankly in such a group than they could before the entire church. And if they could together reach an agreement, their combined influence would most certainly swing the judgment of the larger group.

The contest of minds at this private meeting was intense. Paul laid before them the gospel he preached: God is the God of all men. All men, both Jews and Gentiles, have sinned against him, and stand guilty and condemned before his righteousness. No man by his own efforts can earn salvation; but God in his mercy has made atonement for sin through the death and resurrection of Jesus, so that forgiveness is freely offered to all who believe in Jesus. Since both Jew and Gentile are saved through the mercy of God and not through their own good works, then keeping the Jewish law is as unnecessary as it is impossible. Neither circumcision nor uncircumcision has any meaning in one's relationship to God.

"Paul," said Peter, "we are cordial to your view that it is not necessary for Gentiles to be circumcised in order to be saved. Neither can we yield to the extreme demand that the Gentiles should keep the whole law as the Pharisees interpret it. But this question involves a matter of practical importance. If Gentiles are to be entirely freed from the law of our fathers, what is to assure that they will make a clean break with their pagan customs, and that heathen immoralities will not creep into the Church? You are aware that I agree with your views, since I preached the gospel to Cornelius, who was uncircumcised. But Cornelius, we must remember, was a God fearer; and while he was not circumcised, he was strongly attached to the Jewish faith, and living among Jews. But for Gentiles outside Palestine, who are less rooted in Judaism than he, might not circumcision symbolize a complete break with their past? Would not the law help to keep them from sinking back into heathen ways?"

"The problem you raise is a real one," Paul granted, "but it will not be solved by circumcision. Jeremiah even in his day saw the weakness of the law, and saw that it was necessary for God to put his law in men's minds and inscribe it in their inner lives. Love for Jesus is a surer guarantee of moral living than the law can ever be."

Peter and the others saw that Paul was right in principle, but they were hesitant to carry the principle to its logical conclusion in practice.

"Not everyone sees this as clearly as we do," Peter argued. "There are many more Jews than Gentiles in the Church. These strict Pharisees who believe are a part of the Church as well as the rest of us. It may, therefore, be necessary to make some concessions for their sakes, and demand less than the ideal in facing an actual situation."

"To yield anything to them is to yield all," Paul objected. "Christ has replaced the law. It was merely a guardian to conduct us to Christ. But when we reach Christ, the guardian is no longer needed. To concede anything to the law is to say that Christ is not sufficient. Compromise would be fatal to the faith."

To Paul's judgment Peter yielded. But the issue was brought to sharper focus by the presence of Titus. Granted that it was not necessary for Gentiles in Antioch to keep the law, would it not be well to have Titus circumcised here in Jerusalem so as to avoid offending the Pharisaic party?

"It is our judgment that Titus should be circumcised," insisted James, backed by Peter. "This will show to your opponents that you are willing to take their wishes into consideration. Such a gesture of regard for their convictions will relieve their emotional tension, and may soften their attitude toward the problem you are facing at Antioch."

Paul would not listen to this for one moment. "You do not satisfy the lion's appetite by throwing him bits of food," he contended. "You merely increase it. Should we circumcise Titus, the whole case is lost. Both they and others of their view would interpret that to mean that we had yielded the principle to them. A precedent would be established which would control the question in all future time. The cause is too dear to run such a risk."

"It might be well, then," urged Peter, "to send Titus away. The presence of an uncircumcised Gentile so offends the customs of the Pharisaic Christians that they cannot reason calmly. You will come nearer to winning your case without him present."

"Never!" retorted Paul. "We will hold our ground and use Titus as our example. They argue that a man must be a Jew to be a Christian. That ties the gospel to one nation. It does not offer good news to men as men, but only to men as Jews. It implies that to become a Jew is superior to faith in Jesus Christ. That is to be false to the gospel. Titus is not a Jew, yet he believes in Jesus. He is a worthy Christian. This demonstrates that Judaism can add nothing to Christianity, and that the gospel is free to go to the whole world without the restrictions of Judaism."

This bold and heated challenge decisively settled the question at the private meeting. There sat Titus, second to none in love for Christ, a living testimony to Paul's gospel that Christianity was not a Jewish sect but a world religion. Argument was ended. A Gentile could be a Christian without becoming a Jew.

All that remained now was to meet again with the elders and the entire church to persuade them to Paul's view. With the three leading apostles already won over, Paul had little doubt as to the outcome. Interest in the question ran high, so that at the time appointed a large crowd of people gathered to hear the discussion. In order to prevent the Pharisaic party from feeling that they had not been given opportunity to present their side of the question, a full airing of their views was permitted.

"God made his covenant with the Jews, not the Gentiles," they argued.

That was answered by reference to the new covenant spoken of by Jeremiah, a covenant not of outward Jewish ceremonies but of inward love and obedience toward God. These a Gentile could have as well as a Jew.

"But Jesus was a Jew," continued the Pharisees. "Jesus kept the law himself. He said that he had not come to destroy the law, but to fulfill it. He counseled his workers not to go to the Gentiles, but only to the lost sheep of the house of Israel."

This form of argument was countered by a reminder that Jesus' behavior while here in the flesh was not meant to bind all future generations. Before the cross and the resurrection had made redemption clear to the Jew, it would have been meaningless to carry on a Gentile ministry. The risen Lord, however, had told them to make disciples of all nations. Furthermore, Jesus' attitude toward the Pharisees' idea of keeping the law could be seen in his denunciation of the Pharisees, and in their rejection of him.

When the Pharisaic party had been given ample opportunity to present their case, Peter arose and began to swing the argument in favor of Paul's gospel. "Brothers, you are all well aware that God chose me to take the word of the gospel to the

Gentiles in the home of Cornelius. They heard it and believed. God cleansed their hearts by faith just as he did ours. In this God attested that he makes not the slightest distinction between Gentile and Jew. Why, then, do you insist in imposing a yoke that neither our fathers nor we ourselves were able to bear? No, it is by the grace of the Lord Jesus that we are saved, just as they are. Keeping the law will save neither them nor us."

Taking quick advantage of the opening afforded by Peter's appeal, Barnabas recounted many of the marvels the gospel had worked among men who had believed in Christ but had not kept the law. Paul kept as much in the background as possible. He did not want the case to be prejudiced by the personal animosity of the Pharisees toward him, whom they considered a turncoat Pharisee. Yet, at the conclusion of Barnabas' remarks, he added the weight of his own testimony to the mighty working of God's Spirit apart from the law.

When Paul finished speaking, the air was tense. The extreme Judaizers could sense that the case was going against them. But as they were casting about in their minds for some way to shift the course of events, James intervened with the decisive word. "Brothers," he said, "Simon has rehearsed how God visited the Gentiles that they too might bear his name. To this agree the prophets who spoke of 'the Gentiles who are called by my name.' Hence, in my judgment, we ought not to throw fresh difficulties in the way of those Gentiles who are turning to God. In order, however, to guarantee that they make a complete break with pagan religious practices, I suggest that we write to them, asking them to abstain from whatever has been contaminated by idols, from sexual sins, from eating the flesh of strangled animals, and from tasting blood. They will recognize that these restrictions are fitting, for in every city even the pagans are familiar with the extreme difference between their religions and customs and those revealed by the true God."

This word of James, who as head of the Jerusalem church spoke with authority, silenced the opposition. His proposal was in the nature of a mild compromise, but in reality it embodied a clear-cut victory for Paul. The demands of the Pharisaic party were completely ruled out. But more than that, the removal of circumcision as a requirement freed the Gentiles from all bondage to Jewish law. The compromise involved in the restrictions suggested by James was not objectionable to Paul, because it in no way denied the main principle for which he was contending. Common dietary restrictions would make it possible for scrupulous Jewish Christians to eat with Gentile Christians, which was of great importance inasmuch as the common meal was the center of the worship and fellowship of the Early Church. The abstaining from eating food that had first been offered to idols was not essential, but Paul was willing to tolerate it since it helped to sharpen the difference between Christianity and paganism. Sexual impurity, of course, was as abhorrent to Christianity as to Judaism.

So, although not without misgivings on the part of the Judaizers, the apostles, elders, and congregation overwhelmingly accepted James's proposal. Titus was given the right hand of fellowship. A decision was made to embody the agreement reached in a letter to be sent to the church at Antioch, and to reinforce it by sending Judas, called Barsabbas, and Silas—prominent members of the Jerusalem church—as personal emissaries to deliver the document. The letter read:

"The brethren, both the apostles and the elders, to the brethren who are of the Gentiles in Antioch and Syria and Cilicia, greeting. Since we have heard that some persons from us have troubled you with words, unsettling your minds, although we gave them no instructions, it has seemed good to us in assembly to choose men and send them to you with our beloved Barnabas and

Paul, men who have risked their lives for the sake of our Lord Jesus Christ. We have therefore sent Judas and Silas, who themselves will tell you the same things by word of mouth. For it has seemed good to the Holy Spirit and to us to lay upon you no greater burden than these necessary things: that you abstain from what has been sacrificed to idols and from blood and from what is strangled and from unchastity. If you keep yourselves from these, you will do well. Farewell."

Word of Paul's return to Antioch immediately brought together the whole congregation. The look of joy on the faces of Paul and Barnabas, and the geniality of Silas and Judas, indicated to all that the party had returned with a happy conclusion to the mission on which they had gone. As soon as personal greetings had been exchanged, Silas read the letter from the Jerusalem church. Gratitude was too deep for many words, but moist eyes bespoke the spontaneous feeling of many hearts. The gospel was free to all men. It was offered to all, regardless of race or station in life. And, more than that, Jew and Gentile were one. The unity and peace of the Church had been maintained. All who loved Christ were knit into a fellowship that rose above all differences.

Never was a group more cordial to any speakers than were the Antioch Christians as Silas and Judas encouraged and strengthened them in the faith. Together they worshiped, prayed, and considered how best to take the gospel to all men. As the time of departure drew near, it was with reluctance that the two Jerusalem emissaries were sent off with greetings of peace to those who had sent them.

Paul and Barnabas stayed on in Antioch, tirelessly teaching and preaching, working unceasingly for converts to Christ and for the deepening of the knowledge and faith of those who were converted. But they worked now with surer courage.

Their battle for freedom had been won. Christianity could now go to the ends of the earth, and win the hearts of men of every nation, race, or culture. Victory for Paul in this initial battle set the stage for the greater battle—the world for Christ.

PART THREE

The Conquest

CHAPTER 7

A New Front

AFTER SOME WEEKS in Antioch following his return from Jerusalem, Paul began to grow restless. What was happening to the little groups of Christians he had left in the cities he had visited? Peace reigned in the brotherhood at Antioch since the Jerusalem conference, and the future of the church there was assured. But what about Antioch in Pisidia? Iconium? Lystra? Derbe?

"They are like sheep in the midst of wolves, Barnabas." Paul shuddered as he said it. "There are so few of them. They have known Christ for such a short time. Beaten down by pagan ridicule, harassed by bigoted Jews, confused by false teachers —they cannot stand alone. Let us go back to visit them in every town where we preached, and see how they are faring."

"I should like to go," replied Barnabas. "John Mark is in Antioch now. Let us take him with us."

"John Mark"! The words struck Paul like a lancet! "John Mark"! How it all came back! Perga . . . throbbing head . . . shaking fever . . . mountains and robbers ahead . . . the world for Christ . . . . And John Mark, the youngest and healthiest of them all, whimpering and sulking! Paul's eyes seemed for the moment blinded again with pain, and all he could see was John Mark sailing away on ship deck—weakling, coward, deserter!

"John Mark shall not go, Barnabas," Paul finally spoke. "He deserted before we had faced any real hardship. How would he have stood up under a clubbing in Iconium and a stoning in Lystra? We need a helper who will not desert us when we need his help most. John Mark is not our man."

"He is older now, Paul. Youth has its follies but grows out of them. He will not desert us again."

"He will not desert *me* again," replied Paul. "He shall not have opportunity to do so."

"You mean—" Barnabas paused. "You mean, then, that you refuse his company?"

"I mean just that."

Barnabas grew a little pale. His lips tightened. Slowly it dawned upon him that he and his dearest companion were differing sharply for the first time. They had stood together through weariness, hunger, illness, persecution, the misunderstanding of other men. Now—he could hardly believe it—the ties that bound them were stretching and seemed about to snap. Barnabas knew Paul well enough to know that he would have to yield to his judgment or the break would be complete. Paul was not one to be moved from his position. The prospect of a final break wrenched Barnabas' soul. But he soon found that they could not bring their judgments into line. Paul was so obsessed with the mission before him that he felt he could not risk harming it with a weak helper. Barnabas, on the other hand, had set his heart on Mark. He believed in him; he felt that he must be encouraged, that he would be a help rather than a hindrance to their mission. This, added to the ties of kinship, made it impossible for him to desert John Mark.

"I must stand by the young man, Paul. He will prove himself worthy. With him, I will gladly go with you to visit the churches. Without him, I cannot go."

Paul was abrupt. "Then we part. If your concern is more for your cousin than for the churches we founded in Asia, I will seek other companionship for the journey."

Barnabas felt the sting of this keenly. But he did not yield. He took John Mark and set sail for Cyprus, the land of their birth, to revisit those to whom they had preached on their former journey.

Paul was now faced with the necessity of choosing a new traveling companion. He needed someone who combined courage, zeal, common sense, and kinship of spirit with him and his mission to the Gentiles. He was not long in choosing his man. Silas, after his return to Jerusalem, had revisited Antioch, and was there at the time. Paul had been drawn to him during the Jerusalem conference, and had been impressed with his ability and spiritual depth when he came as an emissary to deliver the Jerusalem letter to the Antioch church. He was a moving preacher, a man of sound judgment, wholly committed to Christ, and convinced that the gospel should be offered to Gentiles without their becoming Jews.

So, with the blessing of the Antioch church, Paul set out with Silas to visit the friends he had made on his former journey. Because Barnabas and Mark had gone to Cyprus, Paul chose to turn northward from Antioch and work his way to Asia Minor by land. Up the coast they went; through the Syrian Gates, through which four and a half centuries before Xenophon had marched his "Ten Thousand" toward Persia; past Issus, where Alexander more than three and a half centuries before had fought one of his greatest battles; across two rivers; past Tarsus, the scene of Paul's youth; through the Cilician Gates; along the ancient road leading to Derbe, the final point of his first journey, to which he had come from the other direction. The two months consumed in making this journey of three hundred and fifty miles on foot gave them time to visit all the churches along the way that had sprung up here and there through the labors of other men.

Surprise blended with joy in the churches of Derbe, Lystra, Iconium, and Antioch, when the travelers made their appearance. Paul listened eagerly to the reports of events since he had been there. The new Christians heard with equal interest Paul's story of the Council of Jerusalem and the freedom that was won for the Gentiles there. The word of Silas added to Paul's confirmed the report and gave them a further sense of oneness with the Jerusalem church. At Lystra, Timothy, who had grown to young manhood since Paul's former visit, was added to the missionary party. He was a devout young man, and would be of great service both as a companion and as a helper.

After revisiting all the churches founded on the earlier journey, the three set out across the mountains north of Antioch in Pisidia to carry their message into new territory in the province of Asia. Paul felt that, to make his efforts count for the most, he should seek to establish work in strategic locations, which would in turn become centers from which the gospel might spread to other towns. Ephesus, the leading city in the province, was the place toward which his mind naturally turned. And yet, though from the standpoint of human reason his path should have led to Ephesus, he had a strange inner prompting to abandon his intention and go elsewhere. So he decided to turn eastward into the province of Bithynia, convinced that God did not want him to preach in the province of Asia. But for some reason the same inner urge that prevented him from going to Ephesus made him uncomfortable about this decision. He was perplexed. His own best judgment seemed to be in conflict with the Spirit of Jesus, who was leading him, and he could not determine the reason. He turned westward into the province of Mysia, and, hardly knowing why, found his way to the port of Troas on the Aegean Sea.

By this time he was weary and discouraged. Since leaving the church at Antioch in Pisidia, he had traveled on foot nearly four hundred miles on a journey that seemed to him fruitless. His purpose was to find new places to preach his good news about God. But his effort had been to no avail. He was consumed with desire to preach his gospel, yet bound by a strange inner restriction from preaching it in the places he had recently visited. God in his heart seemed to say, "Speak!" and yet at the same time God seemed to be saying, "Do not speak!" The contradiction was too much for him. Heat, exhaustion, perplexity, discouragement—these overcame him, and he fell ill in Troas.

As Paul lay ill, Timothy went to seek help. He finally located a physician of good reputation named Luke—a native of Philippi in Macedonia, who had come to Troas to set up his practice. Luke had spoken but a few words with Paul before he sensed that he was treating no ordinary patient. Paul's body was weak, but his mind was keen, and his flashing eyes revealed an unusual vigor of spirit. Paul, too, was peculiarly drawn to this stranger who had come to try to bring him relief. He had an open face, a gentle bearing, a winning modesty, a brilliant mind, and a winsomeness that made Paul feel that he was a friend though he had never met him before.

"From where do you come, friend?" asked Luke.

"I am a native of Tarsus in Cilicia," Paul answered, "but my present journey has brought me from Antioch in Syria."

"Antioch in Syria—it is a long way. Travel exhaustion has overtaken you. A trip like that sometimes breaks the strongest."

"I shall be well soon," Paul ventured. "I travel much, and am used to it. I have lived through worse illnesses."

"What brings you to Troas?"

"I am a messenger of good tidings from God."

"I see that you are a Jew. A traveling rabbi, I suppose?"

"A rabbi, yes. But more than a rabbi. I have good news that the rabbis do not teach."

"The rabbis have good news that others do not teach," said Luke. "Their righteous God, their lofty morals, their hope of a divine Deliverer coming to set the world right—all this appeals to many of us who seek the truth."

"My good news is that the divine Deliverer has already come! In Jesus of Nazareth, God has come into human life as a man. Men killed him, for they did not recognize God in him, and they thought his claims blasphemous. But God raised him from the dead. His resurrection from the dead proves his claims true. He lives now and reigns at the right hand of God. He offers redemption to all who will believe on him. What the rabbis are looking for—has happened!"

Luke came again and again during Paul's convalescence to discuss religious questions with him. At length he became convinced of the truth of Paul's good news. With joy he embraced the Christian faith. His quest for truth had led him, by the accident of Paul's illness, to Jesus.

No sooner had Luke reached his conviction that God had come to men in Jesus than he insisted that Paul must take the good news to his home in Philippi. Of this Paul was not immediately certain. There was such a thing as extending the lines too far and weakening the movement rather than spreading it. Then, too, he had been so perplexed by the lack of openings for his ministry in the long trek he had just taken that he was waiting for some sure word of guidance as to the next step.

As Paul pondered this question, he dreamed one night. In his dream, he saw a man of Macedonia standing before him, and appealing,

"Come over to Macedonia and help us."

Paul was convinced that his vision of the man from Macedonia was the voice of God confirming Luke's judgment that he ought to cross the Aegean Sea to European soil. Immediately, therefore, both Paul and Luke began to lay plans to make the trip.

"Timothy," said Paul, "comb the wharf for sailings to Macedonia. We must be on our way as soon as possible."

"No, Paul," objected Luke. "Leave arrangements to me. I have friends whose business keeps them in touch with sailing ships. They can tell me quickly what we may hope for."

Three days later, just at daybreak, the four of them—Paul, Silas, Timothy, and Luke—boarded a small sailing vessel headed for Neapolis, the seaport of Philippi. The dock was alive with activity, getting the final bits of cargo aboard and arranged for proper balance. When the cargo was made fast so that it could not shift position in a rough sea, the captain

gave the signal to sail. The ropes were untied. Long poles were used to shove the boat away from the dock. With long oars the boat was slowly maneuvered into position to catch the wind.

"Spread sail!" shouted the captain.

As the muscles bulged in the arms of the seamen who tugged at them, the stiff-fibered ropes sliding through the crude pulleys screeched and groaned. The limp sails opened. Finally a brisk morning breeze caught them, and with a loud flap cupped them into shape. The ship began to yield to the steady pressure of the wind. It cut its way through the waves, silent but for the lapping of water on the sides of the hull and the spirited conversation of the sailors. The steady breeze carried them northward and westward with amazing speed. It was a day made for sailors.

They made such progress that by nightfall, when the evening calm began to settle and the water took on a solid, glassy look, they slowly came to dock at the island of Samothrace. After spending the night in a crude hostel ashore, they embarked again early the next morning. The wind favored them once more, so that just at sunset they tied up at Neapolis. It was eight or nine miles from the seaport to Philippi, a journey on foot of two and a half to three hours, so they decided to put up for the night at Neapolis, and to go into the city the next morning.

As Paul lay on his hard pallet that night, a multitude of thoughts crowded his mind and made sleep difficult. Heretofore his vision had been limited to the provinces of Asia Minor. But here he was on European soil—with the whole world before him! Now he knew why the Spirit of Christ had discouraged him from preaching in the provinces of Asia and Bithynia. He had a wider work in mind for him. For the first time, Paul was seized with the clear confidence that Christianity could win the whole Roman Empire—that Christ could conquer all that Caesar ruled, and more. It was a breath-taking experience, that first night on European soil, and he could hardly wait for the light of morning in order that he might be on his way.

The road from the coast to Philippi wound its way through

a slight depression between two rows of hills which shut the city off from the sea. As the travelers passed a large marsh to the left of the road, the city, situated on a steep hill, came into view. Other travelers of importance had skirted that marsh in earlier days. The city had been made a frontier fortress by Philip of Macedon in the middle of the fourth century B.C. It was from there that Philip's famous son, Alexander the Great, had set out to conquer the world. Less than a century before Paul entered Philippi, Antony and Octavian had there avenged the death of Caesar by defeating the armies of Brutus and Cassius. No one could have guessed as he saw this quartet of unknown travelers skirting that historic marsh that what they were to do in Philippi would outlive the achievements of their famous predecessors!

Luke's parents had died, but he found lodging for the group with relatives. There was no synagogue in Philippi, for the Jewish colony there was very small. Luke remembered from his boyhood, however, that a small group of Jews used to gather for worship on the riverbank outside the city gates where he often went swimming. So on the Sabbath Day they set out in search of the place. Through the city gates they went, across a field to the river, then along its bank. There were boatmen, fishermen, strollers, idlers—but where were any worshipers?

"There they are!" suddenly Paul remarked, pointing to several women seated in a circle on mats in the shade of a spreading tree, with a scroll open before them.

"Peace be with you," Paul addressed the women as he and his companions came near.

"And peace be upon you," they replied.

"The Lord our God is one Lord," Paul spoke the opening words of the Jewish creed.

Immediately every face lighted up.

"We are strangers to this city," said Paul, "but we worship the Lord and are seeking others who worship him."

"You have found the only worshipers of the true God in this city," spoke up one of the women. Her features were strong, her manner refined, and her garments rich. "For fifteen years I have lived in this city, and have seen no other worshipers of the true God than these and their husbands. Some of them are away on business and some are on a pilgrimage to Jerusalem."

Her name was Lydia. She was by birth a Gentile from Thyatira. She had come to Philippi with her husband, who was a merchant selling the dyes and dyed garments for which Thyatira was famous. At his death, Lydia took over the business. By shrewd management she had been able to prosper and to maintain the large dwelling that her husband had left her. In her grief over her husband's death she had turned to the mystery religions for comfort. She underwent elaborate secret rites of initiation, designed to secure union with the gods and immortality. This brought her some comfort. But the immoral practices of some of the devotees offended her, and the hope she found was vague, not certain. About this time she opened her grief to the wife of a Jewish merchant friend. Through her she was led to reverence the God of the Jews. Now, as a woman of influence, she was the leading member of the small group who met each Sabbath to pray at the riverside.

Paul announced himself to the group as a rabbi and began to reason with them about Jesus. The women were skeptical at first. Who were these wandering teachers? "The stock of Israel, of the tribe of Benjamin." That sounded good. . . . What were their credentials? Oh, yes—Gamaliel! We know of him. And you were his pupil? How wonderful! . . . "But our faith does not rest on human wisdom, but on the power of God." Strange words . . . And what was the quality of the character of these men? Were they impostors? Were they deceivers who taught for gain? "We take no man's goods nor money. We have left home, loved ones, friends. We have traveled, hungered, suffered, been persecuted—for love of Jesus. We come only to bring you good news of God.". . .

Lydia and her friends did not see the light. But they would hear more! Several Sabbaths were spent in opening up the truth about Jesus: God become man; Messiah must suffer—*did* suffer; God's love—a cross; God's victory—the resurrection; God's continuing work in the world—the Holy Spirit, the Spirit of Jesus in the Church; God's purpose—to sum up all things in Christ through his Church.

At last the light broke. Lydia believed. She would be baptized, with her whole family. Lydia—Paul's first convert in Europe! The course of providence that day was set in a westerly direction.

"You must come and stay at my house," Lydia insisted after she had been baptized. She would thank God by caring for God's messengers.

"You have our thanks," Paul replied, "but our needs are fully met and we are comfortably housed. We aim not to be a burden on anyone."

"But you must be my guests. You will honor my home by your presence."

At this, Luke spoke up. "Paul and his friends are my guests. I urged them to come to Philippi. You must not now rob me of the joy of being their host."

"But you are one of those who have brought us the truth," Lydia replied. "You too must come. You are all to be my guests. If you are convinced that my faith is genuine, you must all come and stay at my house."

There was nothing to do but to yield to Lydia's insistence. Her dwelling was very large, set off from the street by a high wall, through which one entered by a beautiful gate. A straight, formal walk led from the gate to a central opening in the house. Through this opening could be seen a large interior court, surrounded by the house on three sides. A colonnaded portico two stories high graced the entire length of the house on each side. A stairway led to the balcony from which the second-story rooms were entered. A large pool, overlooked by a marble statue, formed the center of the broad stone court. Beyond the house lay a formal garden, with gnarled trees, flowering shrubs, and well-kept hedges. Here Paul and Silas and Timothy and Luke came to live. From this headquarters they directed their work, ofttimes speaking to groups who came to the house, at other times holding public meetings in the market place.

Their efforts met with marked success, particularly among the devotees of the mystery cults, among whom Lydia had many acquaintances because of her former association with them. They were ready to listen to the gospel, for there was nothing about their beliefs that forbade them to investigate other teachings. In fact, many of them, in their search for security in a baffling world, tried to make assurance doubly sure by being initiated into several cults at once. In dealing with these Lydia was of great help, for she knew the workings of their minds and the yearnings of their hearts from the inside.

"These people are groping for something real," Lydia insisted in her long talks with her new friends. "I know. I was once one of them. I know their sense of insecurity, their fears, their hopes. The triumph of the Romans has discredited their old national gods. The ties of race and nation by which they have been anchored have been cut by forcing everyone into one world empire. They seem to be swallowed up as individuals like drops of water in a great ocean of humanity, until their own lives count for nothing. Life for them is brutal, sensual, degraded. They are tossed in a raging sea in a bark too weak to ride it out, and no harbor in sight.

"For me," she continued, "there was some escape in my home, for we had both wealth and love. We built a little world of our own, shut in from the sordidness of life without by the four walls of our house. But then—death came and smashed the walls of that refuge. Then I was exposed not only to the rigors of the world from which I had sought escape, but to the terrors of the unseen world. Frightening questions which I had shut out of my mind before haunted the night hours for me. Was my husband still alive in the world beyond? If he were alive, was he better off or worse off than I? Is death release, or a worse imprisonment? If death makes one a plaything of the gods in a dark torture chamber, as many believe, is there any final escape, or does this last forever?

"In this state of mind—fearful, hopeless, lost—the mystery religions found me. And though I discovered later that their answer to my need was not adequate, yet they knew my problems. The light flickered and went out before it led very far, but it pointed in the right direction.

"I shall never forget the momentary exhilaration when I went through the rites of initiation. The slaying of the bull, the dripping of his blood over me as I stood in the sacred enclosure below, the eating of the sacrificial meal and drinking of the sacramental cup—all this, I felt, made the life of the god mine. I felt I was known to the god as a person; his life force became mine; I was immune from harm. I was let in on the secret of life's meaning known only to those who were initiated. I would live forever!"

"What led you to doubt the mystery religions?" Paul drew her out.

"The influence of my Jewish friend Naomi, of whom I have told you, was the thing that caused the final break," Lydia replied. "But I had had doubts even before she helped me. The question that plagued me after the emotion of the initiation began to wear off somewhat, was this: If the old gods in which I trusted failed, what assurance have I that my new faith will not likewise fail? The symbols of the ceremonies are full of meaning, but suppose there is nothing beyond the symbol! As my old grief and loneliness and fear began to return, I began to feel that the gods I had trusted were not real, but were merely the projections of my own desires.

"It is at this very point, where the mystery religions are weakest, that I find the Christian faith strongest," Lydia continued. "It was that which first convinced me of the truth of Judaism, which gives me confidence in Christianity. Naomi showed me that the God of the Jews is a living God, because he has acted in history in redeeming ancient Israel from slavery and making them a people. He is not a God spun out of men's imaginations, but a God who has come to men from outside them, and worked out his will for them in history. Now, in Jesus, you have again shown me God, working with a reality that I could never doubt. His life and death and resurrection, witnessed by so many, rise above the myths of the mystery religions, and bring God really into touch with human life. And his presence with me, rather than diminishing, seems to be more real as I grow in knowledge of him. You will never know what release you have brought to me in bringing me Christ. God is real; fears are gone; I am certain of the life to come; the light, rather than flickering, grows brighter as I walk in it."

To teaching such as this, many others besides Lydia responded. They had accepted the mystery religions because they had offered them the best solution to the problems of life they had yet found. But Christianity offered something better, and many accepted it with joy. Paul and his companions worked steadily, almost night and day, to keep up with the ever-growing interest shown in the gospel at Philippi.

One day, as they went to the market place, they noticed a crowd of people gathered. Coming near, they saw at the center a wild-eyed girl. Her hair hung about her dirty face in long, matted strands. Her wide-set teeth protruded beneath her upper lip, accentuating the weakness of her lower jaw. Her nails were long, her feet bare. A raucous voice, sounding half human and half animal, called out the fortunes of clients who paid their fees. Here was a woman hoping she would have a male child; a merchant seeking advice on a business deal; a sailor inquiring whether his next voyage would be a safe one;

a gladiator wondering whether he would vanquish his next opponent or be killed himself; a distressed mother seeking confirmation of her hope against hope that her sick child would recover.

As Paul and his friends approached, the master of this depraved girl called out:

"Ho, strangers! Step up! Your fortune for a fee! Tell us your worries. We make tomorrow as clear as yesterday!"

"We are servants of the Most High God," replied Paul. "We need no fortunes told. Rather, we proclaim to you the way of salvation, which will rid you of fears and give you the peace of God."

At this word, the wild eyes of the fortuneteller stared piercingly at Paul and his friends. Suddenly, she rose to her feet, pointed to them with a jerky gesture, and screamed:

"I know these men! They are servants of the Most High God! They proclaim the way of salvation! Ha! God's men! Saviors! Listen to them, you fools!"

A roar of laughter went up from the crowd.

"Bravo! Devil's maid!"

"By the gods! Salvation peddlers, eh?"

Luke took Paul by the arm and moved off down the street.

"An ailing mind, Paul. Let her alone. Men trust her fortunetelling, but think her crazy. She will do us harm and confuse the minds of people about our purpose."

A few days later, however, as they went once more to the market place, the fortuneteller followed them again, calling out as before:

"These men are servants of God! They offer salvation! Hear them!"

With difficulty Paul and his friends shook loose from her and went to their place of daily teaching. This occurrence was repeated day after day, until Paul became deeply distressed by it. Fortunately, his work in Philippi had not been interrupted by hostile Jews as it had been elsewhere. But if the wild following of this demented girl continued, it might handicap his work seriously. Furthermore, he pitied the girl and wished he could help her. As he thought and prayed over the problem, he became increasingly possessed with the feeling that Christ could cure this unfortunate girl and advance his cause among her superstitious followers. One day, as the damsel followed them, shrieking at the top of her voice, Paul turned suddenly and cried out,

"In the name of Jesus Christ, I order the evil spirit out of you!"

The girl collapsed at his feet. She shuddered once or twice, then lay still. The crowd were overawed. Curiosity held them tense for a few moments. Then the owners of the girl shook her violently and called her name. She rallied. Her eyes opened. She was relaxed. Her voice was normal. Her look was sane.

Suddenly, it began to dawn on her owners that the strange powers this girl had used were gone. No more could they collect fees for fortunes. Paul had broken her spell, and with that had broken their business. In fury, they turned on him and Silas. Grabbing them roughly, they cried out:

"Men of Philippi, these strangers spoil our city. They defy our religion. They now have robbed us of the aid of one who can foretell our future. Away with them!"

"They are Jewish swine!" someone called from the crowd.

"Take them to the magistrates, and have them whipped!"

Part of the way Paul and Silas were on their feet; part of the way the crowd surged around them with such force that they were lifted into the air; part of the way they were dragged. Kicks, blows, handfuls of dust, curses—these punctuated the short march to the magistrates' seats in the forum.

Arriving before the officials, the accusers shouted,

"These fellows are Jews who are disturbing our city; they are advocating customs which as Romans we are not allowed to accept or practice!"

"Jews, are they?" sneered one of the magistrates. "We know what to do with Jews. Their backs are good for stripes!"

"Yes," laughed the other praetor, the military belt around his fat stomach bouncing and his sword rattling against his seat, "we have had experience with this sort. Fascinating victims! Their blood spurts at the lash a little higher than most!"

While all this was going on, Paul had tried to announce his Roman citizenship and on that ground protest this action. If only Luke had been there! He might have had it stopped. But in the confusion what chance had Paul to make himself heard? The praetors, small-town officials who did not often have opportunity to express their loyalty to Rome by punishing those who were charged with treason, vaunted their power before the populace and ordered these dangerous men to be flogged.

Their garments were stripped off; they were tied in a stooping posture to low posts near the magistrates' seats; the lashes were applied by the lictors. One, two, three, four—the lashes fell with cruel rhythm. The crowd was in a frenzy. A roar of voices grew like the thunderous cheering of a great stadium crowd. First welts—then blood—then a mass of raw flesh that but a moment before had been human backs!

The flogging ended, one of the praetors commanded the lictors: "Turn these men over to the jailer. Order him to keep them safe. His life for theirs if they escape!"

Off they were dragged to prison. Through the big gates they went; across the prison courtyard; past the outer row of cells; and were finally thrown into a small windowless dungeon in the very center of the prison. Inside, their feet were fastened in stocks. The jailer clanked the heavy bars that closed the one small opening into the cell—an opening little wider than one man and low enough to make one stoop.

The day wore on, and night fell. Their backs were too sore to lie down; their feet fastened in the stocks several inches from the ground made it almost impossible to sit up. Blood had oozed all over them, dried, and caked. Their hair and faces,

covered with grime from being dragged through the streets,
were streaked with mud made by their sweat. They had had
no water, and thirst burned their throats. They could not
sleep. Pain, thirst, bewilderment—yes; but God seemed very
near.

"Our Lord was on a cross, Silas," Paul said quietly. "The
servant is not greater than his Lord. We suffer for his name.
Did he not command us to rejoice when men persecuted us for
his sake?"

"I have been asking myself the old question of the psalmist,
Paul—'Why art thou cast down, O my soul? Hope thou in
God.' And my heart is lifted up."

"Do you remember the verse in that psalm, 'In the night his
song shall be with me'? Let us sing his song in the night."

Feebly at first, but gaining in strength as they went on, Paul
and Silas began to sing some of the psalms they had learned as
children: "God is our refuge and strength, a very present help
in trouble."... "Hear our prayer, O God; give ear to the words
of our mouths. For strangers are risen up against us, and violent men have sought after our souls. Behold, God is our
helper. We will give thanks unto thy name, O Lord, for it is
good. For thou hast delivered us out of all trouble.". . . "We
call unto thee, when our heart is overwhelmed; lead us to the
rock that is higher than we. For thou hast been a refuge for us."
... "O give thanks unto the Lord." ... "O sing unto the Lord
a new song." ... "Bring our souls out of prison, that we may
give thanks unto thy name." . . . "Let everything that hath
breath praise the Lord." . . . As they sang, their spirits rose.
Christ seemed very real, and very near. Their stripes seemed to
be marks of great honor—the honor of suffering for the sake of
Christ.

Suddenly a low, rumbling noise like the roar of distant
thunder was heard. Then the ground beneath them began to
tremble and to sway like the deck of a gently rolling ship! The
noise of falling stones and the creak of swinging bars and

gates added to the excitement. An earthquake! The doors of the prison, wrenched from their positions by the shaking, stood open! The pins to which the chains of the prisoners were attached had been loosened from the mortar between the stones! All stood free, with chains dangling from their wrists and ankles, except Paul and Silas, whose feet were fast in the stocks. Fright overcame the prisoners, so that not one of them attempted to flee.

The jailer, who slept in quarters next to the main prison gate, sprang from his bed and rushed out. The gate was open! The prisoners, he thought, must have escaped. It was his life for theirs! He would rather die by his own hand than be killed for failure in duty. So he pulled his sword from its scabbard and was about to plunge it into his breast.

"Do not harm yourself!" shouted Paul through the narrow slit of his inner dungeon; for the jailer, standing silhouetted in the moonlight, was plainly in his view.

"Do not harm yourself, for we are all here."

"Guards, attention!" shouted the jailer, for by that time all the guards were standing in the court. "Bring torches!" he ordered.

As the lights were brought, the jailer commanded the guards,

"Make fast all the prisoners and see that none escapes!"

Then, taking a torch himself, he hurried across the courtyard, sprang into the inner dungeon before Paul and Silas, and fell on his knees.

"You have caused this," he faltered. "Spare us more!"

"We are but men," answered Paul. "The God of heaven has brought this to pass. He shakes the earth out of its place, and the pillars thereof tremble. Arise! Worship God!"

At this the jailer arose from his knees.

"Julius!" he shouted. A guard came running. "Loose these men from the stocks and take them out to the courtyard."

The jailer made a quick inspection of the entire prison, to

make sure that all the other prisoners were secured so that they could not escape. Then he returned to Paul and Silas.

"Sirs," he addressed them, "I know that you are men who proclaim the way of salvation. What must I do to be saved?"

"Believe on the Lord Jesus, and you will be saved, you and your household as well," Paul replied.

"You must come into my quarters and tell me more of this."

Followed by the entire family of the jailer, Paul and Silas went into his dwelling, where the jailer took water and ointment and washed and dressed their wounds. All the while, they talked about Jesus—his life, his death, his resurrection, his living presence in men's hearts, his redeeming love for all men. The jailer listened with eagerness. He asked questions. He was amazed that Paul and Silas should show deep concern for him, though he was a part of the official machine that had brought suffering on them unjustly. He believed their message. He insisted on baptism. Convinced of the sincerity of their confession of faith, Paul and Silas did not wait until morning, but in the middle of the night baptized the jailer and his entire family into the Christian fellowship.

"You must have food," the jailer insisted, and set to work immediately to prepare for them the best food he could provide. Paul and Silas forgot their sore backs and the agonies of the early night hours in rejoicing that the jailer and his family had believed their word. To suffer for Christ on these terms was a privilege. The jailer, knowing that they would not try to escape, put them for the rest of the night into the guard barracks, where they would be much more comfortable than in the prison.

Early in the morning the lictors who had flogged Paul and Silas arrived at the jailer's office.

"The magistrates send word to release these men," they said. Their superstitious fears had somehow connected the earthquake in the night with their unjustified treatment of Paul and Silas the day before.

The jailer, reluctant to disturb the sleep of his newly made friends, gave orders to a guard to let him know when Paul and Silas stirred. After they awakened, he entered the barracks smiling broadly.

"Good sirs, I have glad news for you. The magistrates have sent to release you! You are free men! But first, you must breakfast at my house. Then go in peace."

"We will confer with the magistrates before we go," replied Paul. "They have beaten us publicly and without a trial, though we are Roman citizens."

"Roman citizens!" At that the jailer's jaw dropped and his eyes stared. "It is not lawful to flog Roman citizens. They have exposed us all to Caesar's wrath!"

"They threw us into prison unjustly, and now they are trying to get rid of us secretly! No, indeed! We cannot leave on such terms. Let them come here themselves and take us out!" Paul continued.

The jailer immediately sent word to the praetors that the men they had flogged were Roman citizens. Fear seized them. What if news of this folly should reach Rome? Roman citizens *flogged!* And what if these men should again stir up a riot, which they could not quell! They must get Paul and Silas out of town as quickly as possible!

Immediately the magistrates set out for the prison.

"Good sirs," they said, "we beg you to leave our city. Begone in peace."

"Why should we leave your city?" questioned Paul. "Do Roman citizens have no rights in Philippi?"

"We did not know you were Romans, good sirs."

"Worthy Roman magistrates do not condemn prisoners without trial, nor flog citizens without knowing it."

"We beg you not to report it, sirs. Let it not come to Caesar's ears!"

"It shall not come to Caesar's ears through us. But we would have you know that Christians are not criminals, nor enemies of peace. We charge you to protect those who have believed in Jesus if vicious men try to do them harm."

"That we will do. But we beg you to leave. Feeling is high in town now. The earthquake is blamed on you. Should you be mobbed again, we may not be able to protect you. We desire no Roman citizen wronged here. We beg you to leave."

"We are ready to leave," replied Paul, "for other towns call us. We shall depart after greeting our friends."

They made their way to the home of Lydia. All who had been won to the faith during their weeks in Philippi gathered to give them a farewell. They prayed; they sang; they rejoiced. Paul and Silas promised to return when they could, and exhorted the others to be faithful to Christ.

The whole group accompanied them from the house, through the streets, out the city gate, and along the road to the river. Just as they rounded the marsh, they looked back and waved a final farewell to Lydia, the slave girl, the jailer, and a score of others. Stripes, imprisonment, scars they would carry to the grave—but the cross had been planted in Europe!

CHAPTER 8

Assault on Athens

Look!" exclaimed Paul breathlessly.

Silas and Timothy, too overawed to answer, stood in rapt silence. They had just rounded a bend at the top of a steep climb where for the first time they saw the city of Thessalonica in the distance. A hundred miles on foot under the eastern sun over the stone bed of the old Egnatian Way had been a grueling trip. But it had been worth it just to see what they then saw.

Thessalonica lay curled around a lovely harbor made by an inlet from the sea. Countless ships lolled lazily around the docks, taking on their cargo. A few white sails in motion across the blue of the bay lent reality to the scene. Behind the city

117

rose the majestic peak of Mount Olympus, which earlier Greek imagination had peopled with gods. It was to this lovely city Paul had turned, because, both as a seaport and as a trade center, it was a strategic place for spreading his gospel.

As the travelers entered the outskirts of the city, they inquired of a passer-by where the Jewish synagogue was. Following directions, they found it in the very heart of the city, not far back from the harbor front. The business opportunities in Thessalonica had brought many Jews there, and they had built a large synagogue as a witness to their faith.

"The God of Israel bless you," said Paul as they met the rabbi who had been conducting classes for the children.

"Peace be upon you," the rabbi replied.

"We are strangers here. Can you direct us to an inn where we may lodge for the night?"

"Gladly. Follow this main street until you come to the watering place. Just beyond that, turn to the left. You will find the best inn in town there, run by a son of Israel. Yeshua ben Izra is his name. You will see it in Hebrew characters above the door."

"We are deeply obliged," answered Paul. "And could you tell us one thing further? I am a tentmaker by trade and desire employment. Are there sons of Israel of that trade in this city?"

"Yeshua ben Izra can tell you. Jewish tradesmen gather at his inn; and if there is a tent seam in town to be sewed, he will know of it. Tell him I sent you."

"God reward you for your kindness," replied Paul.

"And you will come to the synagogue on the Sabbath?" the rabbi called out as they moved off down the street.

Paul smiled and nodded assent.

Yeshua ben Izra was a man with a magic touch. He was the leading Jewish businessman in town and kept the inn more as a center of Jewish trade than for its own sake. He had just the quarters they needed. He knew a tentmaker looking for workmen. He knew all the leading Gentiles of the city. Paul could not have fared better at the hands of anyone than he did with Yeshua. But had Yeshua known the nature of Paul's mission, his help would not have been offered so gladly.

The Sabbath found Paul, Silas, and Timothy at the synagogue service for worship. After the reading of the Law and the Prophets, they were invited, as visiting rabbis, to speak. Paul took the lead in addressing the large group gathered. After some personal words concerning his background and experience, he announced suddenly that Messiah had come to earth, had been killed, and had risen from the dead.

"Think it not strange that this should be," he continued, when he saw the look of incredulity on their faces. "The Scriptures expressly state that the Messiah had to suffer and rise from the dead."

From there he began to open unto them the Scriptures in a way that they had never heard before. Referring to Isaiah's description of the Suffering Servant, he proclaimed it to be a picture of the Messiah. With the skill of a thoroughly trained teacher who knew how to approach the Jewish mind, and the eloquence that only a gifted man with an impassioned spirit can command, he pressed the claim that Messiah had to suffer and rise again. Since that was so, he insisted, Jesus' suffering was the hallmark of his genuineness. He concluded with a mighty exhortation to believe that Jesus was Messiah.

It was a new thought to them. Some of them had heard rumors of Jesus' work in Palestine, but had dismissed him from their minds as an impostor when they heard that he had been crucified. But now—here was a learned, eloquent rabbi, trained by the famous Gamaliel, saying that Jesus was Messiah, teaching that the Scriptures showed that Messiah must suffer! Was it possible? They were perplexed. But they would hear more another Sabbath.

On the second Sabbath confusion reigned in the synagogue. Some thought Paul was right. Others began to denounce the

teaching as blasphemy. As Paul taught, he was frequently interrupted. At times his voice could not be heard above the
heated protests of opponents. Those who desired to hear more,
however, invited him back the third Sabbath. He went, but
found his opponents so violent in their anger and so loud in
their reproach that he had to give up any thought of teaching
longer in the synagogue.

One of the Jews who was persuaded of the truth of Paul's
preaching, Jason by name, insisted that Paul and Silas and
Timothy lodge in his home. Although they labored during the
day in a tentmaker's shop to earn their living, each evening
found them teaching Jason's friends, who gathered at his dwelling. The group grew. Gentiles began to attend and to believe
Paul's word about Jesus. Several of the leading women of
wealth in the city believed. On two or three occasions visitors
came from Philippi, bringing gifts for Paul and greetings from
the Philippian church. It heartened Paul greatly to know that
the work he had started in Philippi was continuing. It also
gave a sense of comradeship to the Christians in both places to
know that others shared their new-found joy. For about five
months the church in Thessalonica grew.

This was the longest period of peace Paul had enjoyed for
some time. But the calm was the menacing quiet before the
storm. The wily tongue of Yeshua ben Izra was finding its
mark.

"Listen to me, sons of Israel!" he often cried in jest to the
crowd of merchants at his door. "I will preach to you good
news. Good news, mark you! Messiah! God's Messiah! God's
dead Messiah! Hear my good news, men! Jesus is Messiah.
Tried! Convicted! Crucified! Rotting in the ground! He will
save Israel from Rome! How many believers have I this morning?"

An uproar of laughter punctuated his caricature of Paul's
preaching. Wild gestures and cunning eyes set his blasphemy
in a vivid framework. And when he paused to spit for em-

phasis, his hearers were thrown almost into convulsions.

One day, after a particularly hearty bit of mockery, he stopped suddenly, and with serious tone cried out:

"Men of Israel, how long do you hold your peace? These Jesus idiots must be run out of town! Our synagogue attendance falls off. We are made fools in the eyes of Gentiles. The law of Moses is broken. The God of Israel is blasphemed. We must silence them, or respect for the faith of Israel in Thessalonica will be ruined forever!"

"You speak the truth, Yeshua," one of the group replied. "But what can we do? They commit no crimes in the eyes of the law. And what do the Romans care about their blaspheming our religion? They rejoice at that."

"But do you not know what will work with the Romans?" Yeshua came back immediately. "Tramp on Caesar's toes and any Roman will squirm. Just accuse these Jesus idiots of treason to Caesar, and the Romans will do the rest!"

"But they are loyal to the Empire. How can we make a case against them? Roman law does not condemn people on unproved charges."

To this too Yeshua had the answer.

"That is normally true. But just whisper, 'Treason to Caesar,' and they lose their heads. The officers would rather risk violating Roman law than be accused of laxity in condemning disloyalty to Caesar. One means punishment; the other means death. Any fool will risk his back before he will risk his neck!"

Slowly Yeshua's plans began to dawn on his hearers. He continued:

"Do they not call Jesus 'lord'? To the Romans Caesar is 'lord.' Can that not be made to look like treason? Stir up a mob! Set the city in an uproar! Accuse these fellows of having some other king than Caesar! And the deed is done! What better time than now? Let us away to the house of Jason and drag them before the magistrates this instant!"

The group of a dozen or more merchants surged out into the

street hard on the heels of Yeshua. At the corner Yeshua found some idlers of the town.

"Come with us!" he cried. "Help us to capture some criminals who are hiding in a house up here! We may need some husky chaps like you. There's money in it for the first man to lay hands on them!"

A fight to break the dull routine of idleness! And money in it too! What more inviting proposition could have been put to these rascals! Down the street they went with Yeshua and his crowd, grinning hopefully at the prospect of excitement.

Like a stream that gathers momentum with every rivulet that enters it, the group that had set out soon grew into a mob. Most of the mob had no idea where they were going or why. But angry voices, a hurrying crowd, some unusual excitement —who could resist following? By the time they reached the house of Jason, several hundred people trailed the leaders.

Not knowing what was afoot, and fearing to expose himself to the mob, Jason appeared on a little balcony which jutted out over the street from the second floor, to inquire what was wanted.

"Paul!" Yeshua howled. "And his friends! Bring them out."

"They are not here," replied Jason.

"You lie!" was the retort.

"Storm the house!" someone shouted, and the mob surged in through the door. Every room was searched, but neither Paul nor Silas nor Timothy was found. Thus foiled, the crowd seized Jason and some Christian friends who were with him, and dragged them off to the politarchs. By that time nearly everybody in the heart of the city had gathered, until it was almost impossible to quiet the crowd sufficiently for the politarchs to hear the accusation.

"These men who have turned the world upside down have come here also, and Jason has received them; and they are all acting against the decrees of Caesar, saying that there is another king, Jesus."

This was a disturbing indictment. It alarmed the mob, for they feared any disloyalty to Caesar. It might lead to the surrender of the freedom that the Romans had allowed their city. Added to this, the rulers were caught in a difficult position. They knew enough of Paul and his followers—some of whom were influential people in the city—to believe that his teaching was not subversive. On the other hand, treason was a serious charge, and if they should dismiss it lightly, they ran the danger of being reported to Caesar as indifferent to his honor. Caught in this dilemma, they conferred at length and reached the decision to let the prisoners go unmolested, but to exact from them a heavy security binding them to keep the peace and to avoid any disaffection from the emperor.

Jason and his friends made arrangements to pay the amount set in the bond, and returned home, thanking God that they were alive. Shortly after their arrival, Paul and Silas and Timothy came in. They were amazed to learn of what had happened, for their work had gone peacefully since they left the synagogue, and they had won many influential converts among the Gentiles. Paul was particularly grieved that his presence in Jason's home had brought trouble on his friend.

A decision as to their future course was hastily made. It was felt by all that any further trouble the mob might stir up would be fatal both to Jason and to the Christian movement in Thessalonica. Jason had given bond to keep the peace. If peace were violated, he and the Christians would be responsible. Inasmuch as Paul had come to the city from the outside and had been responsible for beginning the church there, the ire of the populace would be less likely to be aroused if he were not present. It seemed wise, therefore, for Paul and Silas and Timothy to move on, and to move immediately.

Hurriedly Paul talked over plans for the continuance of the work when he was gone. After encouraging his friends to believe that God would never forsake them, he commended them to the divine care in prayer. In order to protect Paul and his friends if they should be molested, several of the brothers accompanied them out of the rear entrance of Jason's home. Through the darkened back streets of Thessalonica, past the city limits, and on to the road to Berea, they went.

It was a lonely trek through the night, but they tramped on in order to put a safe distance between them and Thessalonica by daylight. A little rest in the early morning hours, and they were on the road again. Another night spent on the way . . . then another day . . . and they trudged wearily into Berea at nightfall.

A happy welcome awaited them there. The Jews of the synagogue, of whom there were many, received Paul's teaching with open minds. They became so interested in his announcement—"Messiah must suffer, and has already come in Jesus of Nazareth"—that they began a daily search of the Scriptures to see whether Paul's teaching was correct. Many were convinced and believed. Besides them many prominent Greeks, both men and women, believed the teaching and entered the Christian fellowship.

This went on for days. It seemed too good to be true. After stonings, beatings, imprisonments, and forced flights, to be received in this fashion was like heaven on earth. Much might have been accomplished in Berea, had not Thessalonica been so near! But along the well-traveled roadway, the news of Paul's success covered the little more than fifty miles between the two cities with remarkable speed. Hatred sent hostile men from Thessalonica to hound Paul in Berea. The stirring events that had forced him to leave Thessalonica were reenacted. A street crowd was whipped into a frenzy. Treason to Caesar was charged. Bodily harm was threatened. Paul's life was in danger. The brothers insisted that Paul flee.

Paul was reluctant to leave such a promising field of labor. His friends, however, would not hear of his staying. But since the hatred of the troublemakers seemed to be particularly directed toward Paul, it was decided that it might be safe for

Silas and Timothy to remain. They could strengthen the
hearts of the brothers and could bring Paul word later of any
change in conditions that might permit him to return. With
all haste preparations for traveling were made. Paul's few be-
longings were bundled together, food for the journey was prepared, and several men were appointed to escort him to Dium,
the nearest port, just seventeen miles away. When they reached
the sea, they found a ship sailing immediately for Athens. They
boarded ship with Paul, therefore, and after a little more than
a week's trip down the coast, set foot on shore at Piraeus, the
seaport of Athens. Here Paul sent the escort back, instructing
them to send Silas and Timothy to join him as soon as possible.

What emotions stirred within Paul as he set foot on the soil
of Attica, the heart of classical Greece! Piraeus was no longer
important as in the days of Greece's glory. But the marks of the
Golden Age remained—covered porticoes, granaries, the fish
market, theaters, temples, statues. Many of these were in dis-
repair, but they stood as silent witnesses to the grandeur that
once was Greece. As Paul walked slowly along the way from
Piraeus to Athens, he could see here and there tumbled re-
mains of the walls on either side of the road. His imagination
rebuilt them as they once stood—solid bulwarks of heavy
masonry sixty feet high, with higher towers jutting out in de-
fiant splendor, along the entire five-mile route from the sea
into the heart of the city. The squalor of the little huts
huddled along both sides of the way contrasted pitifully with
the magnificent Acropolis, which stood like a giant balcony
overlooking the city in the plain below. At the summit of the
Acropolis the shield and spear of the mammoth statue of
Athena glistened in the sunlight. Below stood the stately Par-
thenon, the finest building in Athens. Surrounding it were
clusters of temples, statues, pillars, arches, gates. To the west
of the Acropolis, slightly lower and separated by a steep de-
cline, was the Areopagus, or Mars' Hill, on which the court of

the city sat to try cases—a spot made famous by the trial of Socrates.

As Paul surveyed all this while walking into the city, he was beset by strange feelings. It was the first time in all his missionary journeyings that he had been entirely alone. Self-sufficient though he was, Paul yet had a deep capacity for friendship. To be suddenly thrown into this strange city without a companion touched him with loneliness. Added to this was a suggestion of homesickness. The Athenian temples reminded him of the pagan temples in Tarsus. They carried him, too, back to the Temple in Jerusalem. His boyhood and youth returned to him in a moment. For an instant he felt like a little boy a long way from home, alone.

But his mind soon turned to his churches in Thessalonica and Berea. How were they faring? He had no deep interest in Athens. He had come only to escape the wrath of his enemies. Had that cooled down any? he wondered. Would it be possible for him to return soon? His heart was in Macedonia, not in Greece. If only Silas and Timothy would arrive with a report of developments there! But he knew that it would take several days for his escort to return to Berea, then several days more before his companions could reach him. As he entered the city and secured lodging, his mind was distressed, and he found no rest.

The days before Silas and Timothy came were fretful ones. Waiting goaded Paul's restless spirit. Then too the sight of the idols that filled Athens irritated him. Here, in the city where philosophers had taught that it was superstition to confuse an idol with the god it represented, Paul saw more naked idolatry than he had ever seen before. He saw how right the Jews were in abhorring images of God. To make any material symbol of the One who is Spirit was to blind men to his spiritual nature. It was also to set up something men had made in the place of the God who had made men. Paul's knowledge of the true God was outraged. This mixture of learning and idolatry told him anew that man by his searching cannot find God. He could not keep silence. He must tell them his good news of God in Christ.

Paul could see the emptiness of men's lives here in the center of the world's learning. Their blind groping after gods they did not know revealed a heart hunger that was deep. A restlessness of spirit which kept the Athenians turning from one novel idea to another showed Paul that the centuries of learning which Athens had enjoyed had given the people no solid center on which to build life—no fixed point with reference to which everything else took its meaning. This had led even to the decay of their minds, for the Athens of Paul's day, which was the heir of the great philosophers of the past, was filled with intellectual charlatans. They spoke high-sounding words and tossed ideas about nonchalantly, but little great thinking was done. Their minds were darkened through lack of the truth about God.

Here were men made in God's image, but that image was so defaced and buried beneath layer upon layer of inherited paganism that it was hardly recognizable. Here were men created for the large and expanding freedom of fellowship with God, who were earth-bound, sensual, spiritually dwarfed—men who knew nothing of peace with God or of their eternal destiny. This emptiness of soul in the Athenians, hidden beneath an exterior of learning and sophistication, was vivid and clear to the discerning spirit of Paul. Although his intention had not been to try to start a church here, yet he felt a great urge to try to present Christ to the Athenians—Christ, in whom Paul believed were hidden all the treasures of wisdom and knowledge.

He began first to reason with the Jews and the Gentile proselytes in the synagogue. Then between Sabbaths he wandered about the market place in true Athenian style, conversing with little groups who chanced to come together. The give-and-take of intellectual and religious dispute was daily fare in the market place of Athens. On the porch of a temple, beside a public fountain, within the walls of a shop, in the shade of a public building, at the base of a statue, or before an altar, little groups of men sat matching their wits. Paul joined himself to one and another of these, and spoke of his Christian faith wherever opportunity permitted.

Finally—it was less than two weeks, but it seemed months to Paul—Silas and Timothy arrived. The news they brought from Macedonia was disappointing. The anger of the Jews at Thessalonica and Berea had not abated. The Christians were watched constantly, publicly ridiculed, and occasionally beaten.

"I must return to them," insisted Paul. "They need encouragement. They are young in the faith, and weak. Someone must nurture them."

"But you must not return," countered Timothy. "It is too dangerous."

"Dangerous? What of it? A father does not forsake his children in danger! He goes to them to protect them!"

"But if his going should harm the children more than his staying away?" interjected Silas. "The one thing that would fan hatred into a hot flame would be your reappearance, Paul. The brothers are bonded to keep the peace. If you return, riot will break out. This would outlaw the whole Christian group as enemies of the Empire. It is not right to follow your natural impulse if it harms the Church. You should not be heroic at their expense."

Paul reluctantly agreed. But what ought he to do? Paul's churches were dearer than life to him. They could not be abandoned. A plan suddenly struck him.

"Timothy, are you willing to risk returning to Thessalonica?" Paul asked.

"I am ready to do whatever ought to be done," came the reply.

"May grace and courage be yours, then, my son. You were not a target for their hatred as were Silas and I. Perhaps your going will not endanger the brothers. Return to Thessalonica. Enter the city by night, if possible. Keep under cover as much as you can. Provoke no open scene. But speak comfortably to the hearts of the brothers. Give them assurance of our love and prayers. Steady them through the storm. Be a light in their darkness. And return to me as soon as you are assured they can get along without you. God go with you, my son."

And what of the little church at Philippi, where Paul and Silas had first set foot on European soil? It was decided that while Paul waited in Athens, Silas would go there to carry encouragement and news from Paul and to bring back a report of the Christians to Paul. The three travelers knelt together, committed each other to the care of God, embraced, and parted.

After Silas and Timothy left, Paul became more restive. The longer he stayed in Athens, the more deeply its paganism revolted him. The city abounded in temples, statues, altars, idols. Even the public buildings were sacred to some god. But who were the gods? They were vague, almost impersonal, unknown beings. The God of Paul, who was the loving Father of Jesus, was entirely unknown to them. Nor did their vague religiousness have power to produce moral living on the part of the masses. They were superstitious, sensual, degraded, groping through life like blind men on a treadmill of existence, trying only to soften their fate with whatever escapes they could improvise. Life for them was either all fate or all chance. As they looked at the stars, with their unchanging regularity, they seemed locked in a universe too orderly to change, in which human decisions made no difference. Fate was god, and there was little to do but to make the best of it. On the other hand, as they looked at the uncertainties of their own experience and saw how much of life—both for individuals and nations— seemed to depend on chance, each day seemed as uncertain as the flipping of a coin. Fortune was god, and life was as purpose- less and meaningless as the tossing of a chip on the crest of restless waves. Fate or fortune—what difference? In either case, for the masses life was little more than a compound of fear, despair, resignation, and the countless diversions designed to put trouble from their minds.

The philosophers sought to rise above this despotism of futility and to find some clue to life that would give it meaning, but had little success. The Stoics believed that fate was god, but they tried to overcome the tyranny of fate by making it kindly and good. Fate was virtuous, they held. Whatever it decrees, no matter how hard it seems, is really for one's good. Therefore, one should endure life's buffetings without resistance or regret. The way to virtue is to desire for one's self whatever fate desires for you—to believe that whatever happens is for the best. In matters where one has a choice, he is to do his duty at all costs. In other matters, blind acceptance is the only answer. This was rather lofty doctrine, but it fell short of solving the problem of life's meaning. Do one's duty—yes, but that is exactly what most men are unable to do. Overcome the world—yes, but how is that possible when the world is mightier than you are? How Paul knew the futility of all this! "My own behavior baffles me," he wrote later to his friends in Rome. "For I find myself not doing what I really want to do but doing what I really loathe. I often find that I have the will to do good, but not the power." There Paul laid his finger on the weakness of Stoicism. It was finally a counsel of despair. And even the best of the Stoics concluded that when the gloom of life became too depressing, suicide was a worthy way out. But suicide was an escape to nothing, for the Stoic knew nothing of personal immortality beyond death.

The Epicureans had another answer to men's despair. To them, happiness was the goal of living. Happiness was to be achieved by escape. If there be any gods, they are happy because they do not concern themselves with the world. Men likewise are to achieve happiness by letting the world alone, freeing themselves of all fears and restlessness, and living with inner repose as though life's ills do not exist. "Eat, drink, and be merry," and do not concern yourself about the fears and passions which curse most men's lives, for they are blind superstitions. Where the Stoic encouraged men to conquer the world by courageously accepting whatever it brought, the Epicurean advised men to avoid the world. Let the world alone and it will not hurt you. Where Stoicism offered a counsel of despair, Epicureanism offered a counsel of folly. It was passive, nerveless, unreal, and had only a superficial answer to the problem of life.

The more Paul observed the emptiness with which these teachings left men, the more determined he became to tell them the joyous good news of God's salvation in Christ, who had faced the world and overcome it, and who now offered his victory as a gift to men who would receive it. He began, therefore, to teach more openly and vigorously in the market place. He told those who listened that there was but one God, not many. He told them that this God had visited the earth in Jesus of Nazareth, so that he was no longer an unknown God. He showed them that the God revealed in Jesus was a loving Father, who ordered all affairs for good, so that men were not victims either of fate or of chance. He spoke of the joy in life that Christ offers, so that life's ills are neither to be escaped nor to be merely endured, but are the means by which men share with God in conquering evil in the world, and the tools with which God carves Christlike character out of the raw material of our lives. He told them that Jesus had risen from the dead—that he was thus the guarantee of life beyond the grave. He affirmed that the power with which Jesus had risen victorious over death was now offered to men to live a moral life.

His teaching daily attracted more and more attention. Novel ideas were a favorite sport in Athens, and such teaching as this had never been heard before. Even the philosophers joined the groups with whom Paul reasoned. As they listened, curiosity gave way to ridicule, for the Greeks despised the Jews.

"A learned Jew, by Jove! One is not often seen!"

"Yes, he has picked up a few scraps that fall from Athenian tables! No wit to put them together, of course. But he does well for a beginner!"

"Indeed! Ideas have hard going in vulgar skulls. Transplanted out of their native soil, they don't grow well!"

"An ignorant plagiarizer! A pickpocket of ideas! Ha! He would even steal thoughts!"

"But what a strange Jew! Moses would never own him. He is an exponent of foreign deities, which the Jews do not accept. Who is this god Jesus, and his female consort, Resurrection?"

These philosophers, with all their wisdom, had no understanding of what Paul really meant. The Greek word Paul used to speak of Jesus' resurrection was feminine in form. Since he preached Jesus and the resurrection, they mistook "resurrection" for the name of a female deity.

"Take him before the Council of the Areopagus," cried one, seizing Paul by the arm. "Come along, stranger. Give account of your teachings to the Council. Let them judge of their worth."

They were followed by a crowd of idlers as they wound their way out of the market place toward Mars' Hill. Ascending the steep stone steps up the side of the hill, Paul uttered a silent prayer for God's help. Here, at the center of the world's capital of learning, he was to proclaim his faith. He was to match God's wisdom against man's wisdom. He wanted to do it well, but he knew that he could not meet the demands of that hour by his own strength or cleverness. So, as they went up the hill, surrounded by the confusion of the crowd, Paul was conversing with Christ in the secret places of his heart. His Lord was always with him, but in hours such as this Paul's deepened need led him to a greater awareness of the living presence of Christ. His unseen companion became more real to him than his surroundings. He felt sustained by a strength equal to the task. As his own fears arose to weaken his confidence, he told himself, "I am ready for anything through the strength of the One who lives within me." And his mind was at peace in the knowledge that his Lord would not fail him.

As they reached the summit of the ascent, they stood before the members of the Council, who were seated on stone benches carved out of the rock of the hill. The crowd stood below on the surrounding slopes.

"Now let us know what is this novel teaching of yours, that the Council may judge of it," said the spokesman. "You speak of many things that sound strange to us. Tell us what they mean."

This was a great hour for Paul. From Mars' Hill, as he stood forth in their midst to speak, he could see both the wisdom of man and the folly of man. Art, learning, religion—all were here. But in what contrast! Art at its best; learning at its highest; but religion—a pathetic failure! The human hand and the human mind—Athens was a marvel of what these can do. But the human spirit—at its worst, degraded by idols and debased by sensuality; at its best, hopelessly imprisoned in ignorant worship of an unknown God.

"Men of Athens," Paul began, "I observe on every hand that you are a most religious people. As I was going through your city and scanning your objects of worship, I came across an altar with the inscription, To an Unknown God. Well, this divine nature which you worship in ignorance, I am setting forth to you."

Raising his hand toward the Acropolis, with its cluster of temples and monuments, he continued:

"The God who made the world and all things in it, he, Lord as he is of heaven and earth, does not dwell in shrines made by human hands; nor is he served by human hands as if he needed anything, since he himself gives life and breath and all things to all men.

"Indeed, he is close to each one of us, for in him we live and move and are. Some of your own poets have said, 'For we are also his offspring.' Now as the offspring of God, since we are superior to material things, we ought to know that the God from whom we have come does not resemble gold or silver or stone. God is not the product of human art and invention, as your temples and statues would suggest.

"Since you have made this mistake in ignorance, God overlooks it. But now, since I tell you of the true nature of God, he charges you to repent and turn to him. For he has fixed a day on which he will judge the world in righteousness by a man, Jesus, whom he has appointed. And he has given proof of this to all by raising him from the dead."

The clamor of a hundred voices rose at this. Some threw back their heads in roaring laughter; others shook their heads slowly, tapping the brow; still others curled their lips in disgusted sneers. Above the clatter could be caught a few of the things they were saying.

"Atheist! A god who can't be seen is no god."

"The Jewish god is ugly! That is why they never make images of him!"

"A dead man is going to judge the world! Ha! Climb out of the grave! Rattle his skeleton to frighten bad men! Point a bony knuckle at criminals and have them executed! A dead man on the loose!"

It was Paul's mention of the resurrection that touched off the deepest scorn of the Athenians. To them, the body and the spirit were enemies. The body was earthly and evil; the spirit was good. During this life the spirit was imprisoned in the body and was seeking escape. At death, it was set free from the body. To speak of a resurrection, therefore, and to suggest that a man who had been dead had actually been raised to life again was a monstrosity of thought which deserved no serious consideration. Such teaching was only to be laughed out of court. No intellectual person could accept any such folly.

Paul could not have been heard if he had tried to say more. Nor would further speaking have been of value. Truth is stifled by mockery. So, as one with mock respect said: "This is most interesting! We will hear you again on this same subject!" Paul withdrew from them and found his way back to his quarters. Had they taken him seriously instead of laughing at him, he might have found himself in real trouble with his judges. As it was, they let him go as a harmless fool on whom they had no time to waste.

As Paul sat alone that night and pondered the events of the day, a shadow hung over his spirit far darker than the eerie dimness of his room. Paul was proud by nature, and sensitive. It was never easy to be laughed at, but it was doubly hard to take when intellectual men, whose minds he knew were not one whit better than his own, ridiculed him as an ignoramus and a fool. But more than that it cut him deeply to see how blind men were to his gospel. It all seemed so clear and so reasonable to him. And yet these men to whom he had offered it, who were obviously world-weary, emptyhearted, and in great need, saw in it only folly.

"O God," he cried out, "how can they be so blind?"

And then, as the emotional depression from the afternoon's experience deepened, he began to reproach himself. Perhaps it was his fault.

"If only I had been able to present the truth more clearly, they might have seen," he chided himself. "It was my weakness that lost the day. They couldn't see Christ for me."

The more he struggled with himself, the more the events of the afternoon seemed to spell out one dismal word—failure! Failure seemed to become personalized and to assume the form of a gigantic demon, pointing an accusing finger at him which withered and scorched. His loneliness became desolateness; his disappointment became remorse; his self-accusation turned to shattering guilt. He felt like a condemned criminal in a dark dungeon awaiting his doom. He flung himself down on his knees, and buried his head in his hands, and prayed. He could utter no words, but merely groaned out his misery in a soul struggle too deep for utterance. Even as he prayed the black-ness of despair thickened, and he felt that he was sinking in an abyss of the soul which was bottomless.

Just when he felt as though despair would crush him, he be-came strangely aware of a Presence. He thought he was alone in the room, but there was Another there. And when he could find no way even to voice his prayers, this Other One seemed to be praying for him with great urges of spiritual energy too deep for expression. The darkness began to give way. He had an indescribable feeling of being lifted and carried out of the abyss into which he had been plunged. His loneliness yielded to a distinct sense of intimate companionship. His turmoil van-ished in a quiet peace. The One who had met him on the Da-mascus road again made himself known in a special way. He seemed to be saying to Paul: "Consider, what have the philoso-pher, the writer, and the critic of this world to show for all their wisdom? Has not God made the wisdom of this world look foolish? For it was after the world in its wisdom had failed to know God that he in his wisdom chose to save all who would believe by the 'simple-mindedness' of the gospel message. For the Jews ask for miraculous proofs and the Greeks an intellec-tual answer to everything, but all we preach is Christ crucified —a stumbling block to the Jews and sheer nonsense to the Gen-tiles, but for those who are called, whether Jews or Greeks, Christ the power of God and the wisdom of God. God's 'stupid cross' reveals a greater wisdom than that of men, and his weak-ness a greater strength than theirs." The living Presence did not say these things in words, but somehow in the intimacy of fellowship between them he conveyed truths to Paul so clearly that later the apostle wrote them to his friends in Corinth.

Suddenly Paul was aroused from this mystical experience by a knock at his door! He arose and opened it, to look into the eyes of a stranger whose face seemed vaguely familiar. Oh, yes, Paul remembered now. He had been one of the members of the Council of the Areopagus—Dionysius was his name. Dionysius had been captivated by Paul's address on Mars' Hill, but had lacked courage to stand by him openly at the meeting. He could not put it out of his mind, however, and had come to learn more. Had God really visited the earth in this man Jesus of whom Paul spoke? Had Jesus really been raised from the dead? Is there personal existence beyond the grave for those who believe? Paul reasoned with him long into the night. Finally, the light began to dawn on Dionysius, and he believed Paul's word. Paul's address on Mars' Hill had not been a failure, as he had thought, but God had used it to awaken at least one thoughtful man to the wonder of the gospel. And there were others, among them a woman, Damaris, who came and believed. These new converts brought still others who accepted the truth about Jesus. And so the Christian church in Athens was born.

Encouraging as this was, Paul felt that Athens was not to be the scene of a lengthened ministry. He had come there with the hope of returning to Berea and Thessalonica. Since hatred of the Jews in those cities had shut the door in his face, he felt that he must turn elsewhere. Where should it be? Where but Corinth—the seaside Sodom of the ancient world? Back to Piraeus, therefore, he went to find a boat for Corinth.

CHAPTER 9

𝕭ictory at Corinth

A BANK of heavy clouds made the morning dull and gray.
Standing on the deck of the little cargo ship as it tied up at the
dock in Cenchreae, Paul could see Acrocorinth, the rocky citadel of Corinth, eight and a half miles from the port, rising like
a sentinel guarding every approach to the city. Had the day
been clear, Paul could have seen it from Athens, more than
fifty miles away. For nearly two thousand feet this rugged
promontory thrust its arms up into the sky, and cast a giant
shadow across the plains surrounding it. Near the foot of this,
on a slight eminence, lay the city of Corinth.

In coming from Athens to Corinth, Paul had left the citadel
of culture for the citadel of wealth. Athena, the goddess of the

mind, gave way to Aphrodite, the goddess of the body. In Athens, ideas reigned; in Corinth, emotions were supreme. Learning was king in Athens; lust, in Corinth.

The location of Corinth determined its nature. Poets called it "the city of the two seas," because it lay at the lower end of a narrow isthmus, at some points not more than three miles wide, which separated the Aegean from the Adriatic. With an excellent port on either side, it became the central shipping point in the entire Mediterranean area. Small boats were dragged across the isthmus from one sea to the other on wooden slides. The cargoes of large ships were carried across and loaded on other ships. The commerce of the world flowed through Corinth in a steady stream. This meant wealth; wealth meant luxury; luxury meant depravity.

The depravity of the ancient city was increased in the Corinth to which Paul came. In the second century B.C. ancient Corinth had been besieged by Rome, which completely demolished it and turned this wealthiest city in the world into a rubble heap. It lay in ruins for nearly a century. But Julius Caesar, aware of its strategic location as a military center, rebuilt it. He populated it with freed slaves from all over the Empire— a mixed lot of the dregs of society. These furthered the natural tendency of port cities to degenerate, so that by the time Paul arrived in Corinth, it had become the cesspool of the Roman world.

As Paul journeyed into Corinth and looked about the city, he was depressed by what he saw. Loneliness and idolatry had made his spirit low in Athens. But Corinth depressed him even more. Immorality, debauchery, obscenity—Paul had never seen them so concentrated as here. In writing to the Roman Christians later, he described what he saw in Corinth —"vile passions" . . . "utter filthiness such as debased their bodies" . . . "dishonorable passions" . . . "homosexual lusts" . . . "wickedness, rottenness, greed, and malice" . . . "envy, murder, quarrelsomeness, deceitfulness, and spite" . . . "whisperersbehind-doors, stabbers-in-the-back, God-haters." . . . "They scoffed at duty to parents, they mocked at learning, recognized no obligations of honor, lost all natural affection, and had no use for mercy." All of this washed over Paul's spirit like a wave of stifling filth. He felt weak. He felt sick. He felt as if he had wandered unwittingly into the anteroom of hell.

Could his gospel survive in such a place as this? Could the slender flame of purity burn in such a heavy atmosphere? Was Christian truth able to transform paganism as depraved as this? Of one thing he was sure—if Christianity could work a transformation here, it would be only by the element of *power* in it. Paul's task here was not to enlighten men about the God whom they worshiped in ignorance. It was rather to confront them with a God powerful enough to awaken and redeem moral natures of men who were little more than refined animals. Only Christ and him crucified—the power of divine love made known on a cross—was sufficient. If that failed, there was no other hope. Meanwhile he must support himself.

A tentmaker of the house of Israel—surely there would be one or more in a trade center such as Corinth. He wandered through the streets, peering intently into door after door, seeking some sign of a Jewish tentmaker's shop where he might offer his services. At last, on the hint of a passer-by, he made his way out past the immense open-air theater to the edge of town, near the great stadium where the famous Isthmian games were held. Save for the coveted prize of being a victor at Olympia, every Greek athlete counted a triumph at the Isthmian games the highest goal of life. Not far from the stadium where these athletic heroes were crowned, Paul recognized, through the open front of a shop, a man of his own people stitching together large strips of tent cloth.

"Peace be upon you," Paul spoke in his ancestral language as he entered.

"And peace be upon you," the workman replied, as he ceased stitching and looked up at Paul.

"I am a stranger in this city," continued Paul, "and am seeking work. I am well trained in your trade, and am wondering whether you might need a helper."

"I too am a stranger, but lately come to Corinth," the workman replied. "There is much business here. But since I am just getting set up and have few connections, I cannot tell how much help I shall need. I have orders enough now to give you work for a day or two. After that, we shall have to see what work comes in."

"My name is Saul—Paul to the Gentiles. I am a native of Tarsus."

"Aquila is my name. I have lived long in Rome."

"Rome!" Paul pricked up his ears. "Why did you leave Rome?"

"Have you not heard? Claudius—God curse him—tried to expel all Jews from Rome. My wife Priscilla and I took what we could with us, and decided to come to Corinth as a likely center of commerce where we could ply our trade."

"But Jews have rights in Rome. I am a Roman citizen. How could Claudius expel them?"

"Yes, Jews have had rights in Rome—freedom of religion, freedom from military service, freedom of self-government in questions pertaining to our own customs. But trouble arose, and the edict of exclusion was announced. It couldn't work. Too many Jews to expel. It finally ended only in restricting Jewish gatherings. We, however, did not like to live under suspicion. Further trouble is likely to come on the Jews. If it does, it will fall most heavily in Rome. It seemed more desirable to us to risk the future here. And so we have come."

"What prompted the action of Claudius?" Paul asked.

"Riots among the sons of Israel."

"Riots over what?"

"False teaching in the synagogues. Some travelers returned from Jerusalem with the strange notion that Messiah had already come. Jesus, they call him."

Paul caught a short breath. Then Jesus was already known in Rome!

"The synagogues became fiercely divided," Aquila continued. "The rabbis led a movement to put down the new teaching with violence. Trouble flared. The Romans did not like it. Claudius acted to restore peace."

This gave Paul his opening. His fingers stitched the heavy canvas, but as he worked he drew out Aquila in conversation which gave him opportunity to present Christ to him.

"Do you think Messiah has come?" Paul asked.

"Messiah come?" Aquila echoed abruptly. "How could I believe that? Have you never read the Holy Writings? When Messiah comes, he will dash in pieces the enemies of Israel and break them with a rod of iron. If Messiah has come, how could Jerusalem be subservient to Rome? Is God's Messiah less powerful than Claudius? No, when Messiah comes, he shall rule the nations, and his dominion shall be unto the ends of the earth."

"But Messiah must reign over a *holy* kingdom," continued Paul. "Israel has been unfaithful to God, and stands under his judgment as much as the Gentiles. Have you never read in the Scriptures: 'There is none righteous, no, not one. There is none that seeketh after God; they have all turned aside, they are together become unprofitable; there is none that doeth good, no, not so much as one: there is no fear of God before their eyes'? It was Israel's mission to repent, and to lead the nations to repentance. Since Israel has failed, God has sent his Messiah to create a new Israel. This includes both Jews and Gentiles who repent of their sins and believe in God's forgiveness, who are circumcised in heart and not in the flesh."

This startled Aquila, for it was the same teaching that had stirred up the trouble in Rome. Priscilla too, who had overheard the conversation from an adjoining room, came in to join the discussion. They were lovers of peace, and so had not participated in the quarrels in Rome, but now they had opportunity to talk out the matter freely in the quiet of their own home.

"But how could Messiah be crucified?" they objected when Paul pressed his conviction that Jesus was Messiah.

"If he had been only crucified," Paul replied, "he could not have been God's Messiah. But God raised him from the dead! Since he is stronger than death, he is stronger than all earthly rulers; yes, even mightier than the unseen spiritual agents who control this darkened world from the very headquarters of evil."

Paul's claim that Jesus had been raised from the dead was incredible to Aquila and Priscilla. They said little, but their disbelief was written clearly on their faces.

"I too could not believe this when I first heard it," Paul continued. "In fact, I thought it blasphemy and a lie. So sure was I that it was all wrong that I led the movement in Jerusalem to persecute those who believed it. But as I sought to carry the persecution to Damascus, this One who had been crucified met me and spoke to me. I knew then that he was alive!"

Paul's story of his conversion, as he unfolded it at length, enthralled Aquila and Priscilla. It sounded unbelievable, and yet Paul told it in such authentic tones that they could not disbelieve it. They became so interested that they invited Paul to be a guest in their home. It was not long before they came to accept Paul's message and were baptized as his first converts in Corinth. This encouraged Paul greatly, for Aquila and Priscilla were both strong characters, in whom he immediately saw great possibilities as his helpers.

They discussed at length the best way to approach the Jews of Corinth with this new message. Paul was anxious, if possible, to avoid open conflict, for he wanted to leave the way open to return to Corinth at a future time—something that he could not do at Berea or Thessalonica. He did not know what the future would hold for him after Timothy and Silas had arrived from Macedonia. Hence, he decided, with the approval of Aquila and Priscilla, that it would be best to move cautiously in Corinth. He would argue in the synagogue that it was necessary for Messiah to suffer—that Messiah, when he came, would not conquer the Romans, but would call upon his people to suffer with him for the redemption of the world. But Paul determined not to preach that Jesus was Messiah. That would come later. So each Sabbath Day he went with Aquila and Priscilla to the synagogue and sought to persuade the Jews and Gentile proselytes that Messiah must suffer.

One day Paul suddenly dropped his needle and sprang to his feet. There in the door stood Silas and Timothy! How the words flew back and forth! Paul bombarded them with questions: Had the jailer at Philippi stood steadfast? What of the deranged girl he had cured? What of Jason? And the others? Had the persecution subsided? Had any fallen away from the faith? Were there any new converts? The hours sped on, but they seemed like moments as the three talked, recounting all their experiences since they had separated.

One thing was certain. Paul could not safely go back to Macedonia now. His appearance there would only fan persecution into a hotter flame. He would, therefore, stay on in Corinth. Meanwhile, since he could not revisit Thessalonica, as he had hoped, he would do the next best thing—write a letter. Timothy's report had, on the whole, been good. The Thessalonians were standing firm under persecution. Paul would write of his joy over this, and give them what counsel he could by letter.

"Timothy, go to the market for some sheets of papyrus on which Silas may pen a letter for me."

Paul did not write a neat hand. He formed his letters far too large and they filled the page very quickly. Since papyrus was scarce and expensive, he therefore followed the custom of dictating his letter to a secretary—in this case, Silas.

Paul, Silas, and Timothy send greetings to the church of Thessalonica in God the Father and our Lord Jesus Christ. Grace and peace be with you.

When we mention you at our time of prayer, it is always with a special note of thanksgiving to God. We have felt like orphans during the short season we have been separated. "Out of sight" did not mean "out of mind"; and we have longed ardently to see you again. You are our glory and our joy.

That's how it happened that when I could bear it no longer I decided to carry on alone in Athens, and sent Timothy to strengthen and comfort you. I feared that the tempter had drawn you away from the faith. But now that Timothy has returned and brought us good news of your loyalty and love, I am greatly cheered. I really feel alive again, now that I know you are holding your ground in the Lord.

But there were problems in Thessalonica about which Timothy reported. Paul's enemies had sought to discredit him personally. They said he was a fanatic, a deceiver, a wandering teacher whose motive was to make a living without working. These accusations cut Paul to the quick, for he loved his Thessalonian brothers more than his own life. He answered these charges by appealing to his behavior while he was among them.

You remember, my brothers, our first visit. We had been ill treated and insulted at Philippi. Yet in spite of that, we spoke courageously to you about the gospel of God. Our appeal does not spring from illusion or from impure motives, nor is it based on deceit. We never had recourse to flattery, as you know; nor did we ever fill our pockets at your expense. Nor did we look for honors at the hands of men. Rather, we behaved among you like a nursing mother ministering to her children. Do you remember how we actually supported ourselves by manual labor, working at our trade day and night in order not to be a burden to any of you? You know, as God knows, how upright was our behavior among you. And you received the message not as a merely human message, but for what it really is, a message from God. I know you will be loyal to me, who dealt with you like a father with his children, in spite of the false accusations made by my enemies.

Some pagan impurity had broken out among the Christians in Thessalonica. This was absolutely incompatible with the Christian faith.

God's plan is to make you holy, and that entails first of all a clean cut with sexual immorality. Every one of you should learn to control his body, keeping it pure and treating it with respect, and never regarding it as an instrument for self-gratification, as do pagans with no knowledge of God.

The Thessalonians were troubled about the Second Coming of Christ. It was delayed, and some of the Christians were dying. How could they share in the reign of Christ if they were already dead when he returned? Furthermore, how would those who were still living know when the Second Coming was to occur, in order to be ready for it?

I do not wish you to be left in ignorance about the condition of the Christians who die before the Lord's final coming. You must not grieve for your dead as those do who have no hope of a final reunion. If Jesus died and rose again, since Jesus and his members are inseparable, God will cause those who had fallen asleep in Jesus to return with him. We who are still alive at his coming will have no advantage over those already dead. Both they and we

shall be always with the Lord. And as for the Day of the
Lord—it will come as unexpectedly as a burglar in the
night. But you need fear no alarm. Live like soldiers on
the watch, and you will be ready for it when it comes.
Never stop praying. Be thankful. Steer clear of evil in any
form.

Pray for us, my brothers. Convey my salutation to all
the brethren with the sacred kiss. Read this letter to all.

The grace of our Lord Jesus Christ be with you all.

Silas gave the pen to Paul. In large handwriting he signed
his own name, "PAUL," then handed the sheets to Timothy.

"Go, Timothy, my son—go back to Thessalonica. Deliver
this word from me. Speak comfortably to their hearts. Con-
firm their faith. And after a time, return to me with word from
them. God go with you, my son."

That was all that Paul could do at the moment for Macedonia. Now he must turn his attention to the task at hand. The
reports of Timothy and Silas had greatly heartened him. He
was now convinced that the churches he had founded could
withstand persecution and could carry on in his absence. He
must, therefore, work his hardest here in Corinth, so that from
this crossroads of the world the truth could spread in all directions, and many churches spring up throughout the Empire
which he had no time to found himself. A generous gift from
the church at Philippi made it possible for him to live without tentmaking now. This gave him full time to preach. His
spirit rose to the challenge of this new opportunity, and he set
to work in Corinth with a vigor that exceeded even his strenuous labors in the past. As was his rule, he brought the gospel
to the synagogue.

Paul's message that Messiah must suffer, with which he had
begun his ministry here, was replaced with the announcement—startling to the Jews at Corinth—that Messiah *had* suf-

fered. He had already come, died, and risen from the dead. Messiah was Jesus!

The reaction of the Corinthian Jews was immediate and ran true to form. When the confusion in the synagogue subsided a little, Paul grasped the loose folds of his long garments, shook them violently, and cried out,

"Your blood be upon your own heads!"

"We shall risk it there, and yours too, if you do not leave our synagogue with your blasphemy!" snarled a wrinkled old elder of the congregation.

Further words of the old man were lost in the general hubbub. Raising his hand as a gesture that he wished to say more, Paul finally got them quieted down enough to speak.

"I have spoken words of truth. You have spurned them. As did the men of Jerusalem, so you have rejected your Messiah! The choice is yours! I am not responsible! From now on I leave you and go to the Gentiles!"

With that, he left the synagogue and went home.

From then on life in the Jewish community in Corinth became explosive. When Paul left the synagogue, he had a following. One Titus Justus, a devout Gentile proselyte, offered Paul the use of his home as a meeting place. It was situated right next to the synagogue—a distinct advantage for Paul's work, for every Jew who came to the synagogue was reminded constantly of Paul's message. Then, too, to be thus closely associated with the synagogue avoided any suspicion on the part of the Roman authorities that this was an entirely new religion. They would look on it as a branch of Judaism, which was officially tolerated. Furthermore, since Titus Justus was a Gentile, his home was open to receive Gentiles who were attracted to the new faith. This would not have been true of a Jewish home.

To the Jews, the presence of this rival congregation next door to the synagogue was an outrage. It had to be stamped out—but how? They could hardly carry the case to the Roman courts, for the Christians were not violators of Roman law. But if they took the matter into their own hands, and stamped Paul's movement out by violence, they would be risking their own lives. Had Claudius not driven the Jews out of Rome because of riots over this man "Chrestus"? There was nothing for them to do, then, but to wait their opportunity.

Week after week, as the two groups gathered for worship in such close proximity, the hatred of the Jews deepened. It was climaxed by the conversion to Christianity of Crispus, the ruler of the synagogue. To have the leading member of the Jewish community join the rival group both humiliated and enraged them. Furthermore, many of the Gentiles of Corinth were being won to Paul's faith. It was evident that passion would soon reach the breaking point. Something was bound to give way.

This situation pressed a decision on Paul. Twice now, at Thessalonica and at Berea, the Jews had accused him to the Roman authorities of disloyalty to Caesar. Both times he had been forced to leave. In each city, the persecution of the Christians continued after he left. Would the pattern be repeated here? If so, would it not be better for him to leave before the storm broke? Perhaps if he moved on, tension would subside and the Christian group could survive without him and be less subjected to the possibility of persecution.

It was a difficult decision to make. To leave Corinth just when the door of opportunity was swinging perhaps wider than it had ever done before seemed foolish. And yet, to imperil the future of the movement by staying and embroiling the church in public dispute hardly seemed right. What should he do?

Paul pondered, prayed, sought light in the Scriptures, counseled with his friends. At last the answer came. Reading from the scroll of Isaiah one night before retiring, his eyes fell on these words:

"Fear thou not, for I am with thee; be not dismayed, for I

am thy God; I will strengthen thee; yea, I will help thee; yea, I will uphold thee with the right hand of my righteousness."

Was that a word for him in this hour? He read on: "Behold, all they that are incensed against thee shall be put to shame and confounded; they that strive with thee shall be as nothing, and shall perish . . . . For I, Jehovah thy God, will hold thy right hand, saying unto thee, Fear not; I will help thee."

As Paul slept that night, the Lord appeared to him in a dream, and said,

"Do not be afraid, but speak and do not be silent; for I am with you, and no man shall attack you to harm you; for I have many people in this city."

The sun seemed brighter the next morning. Indecision was gone. No longer need Paul waste his energy on wondering what to do. He could now throw himself without reserve into preaching and teaching in Corinth. This new concentration of effort sharpened the force of his work. Power radiated from him. He became a spiritual dynamo. Pagan lives were touched by the mighty power of Christ. Moral filth was washed away. Idols were abandoned for the living God. Superstition gave way to faith. Ignorance yielded to the truth. In the center of the world's most profligate city was set "a little colony of heaven."

The remarkable progress of Paul's movement convinced the leaders of the synagogue that if he was to be silenced, drastic action would have to be taken soon. So, risky though it was, they decided upon the bold step of mobbing him and accusing him before the Roman proconsul. A new proconsul had but lately been appointed—Gallio, the brother of Seneca—who was known to be an amiable, easygoing type of man. If they could get his verdict against Paul, the whole Christian movement throughout the Empire would be quite discredited. Lesser officials would not lightly set aside the verdict of a proconsul. Officers of equal rank elsewhere probably would accept his verdict to save the trouble of an investigation of their own.

On the other hand, if Gallio were not won over, his amiability could be trusted not to lead him to violence against them. In any case, they felt it was worth the risk. So, for the first time in Paul's career, he was to be haled before a Roman official who had the high rank of proconsul.

With plans carefully laid, a crowd of Paul's enemies assembled before the synagogue at a time when Gallio was hearing cases at the public judgment seat. At a given signal, they swarmed into the house of Titus Justus, seized Paul and dragged him off toward Gallio's court. The prearrangement of the scene brought every Jew in Corinth to the fracas, and they were many. They hoped by the size of the mob and the vigor of their protest to impress Gallio with the seriousness of their charge. Sosthenes, who had succeeded Crispus as president of the synagogue, took the lead in arguing the case before Gallio.

"This fellow is a troublemaker in Corinth," he began. "He incites men to worship God contrary to the Jewish law."

"What care I for Jewish law?" retorted Gallio. "Jewish superstitions do not concern Romans."

"But our ancient Jewish religion is recognized by the emperor," continued Sosthenes. "This man would pervert it. He claims to believe the Jewish religion, but he has introduced a new religion which the Romans do not recognize."

"Has he committed any crime punishable by Roman law?"

Sosthenes could not name any.

"Has he offended Roman manners or customs?"

Again Sosthenes was silent.

Paul made as though he would speak in self-defense, when Gallio cut him off: "I will not hear your defense."

Then, turning to the Jews, he continued:

"If it were a matter of wrongdoing or vicious crime, I should have reason to bear with you, O Jews; but since it is a matter of questions about words and names and your own law, see to it yourselves. I have enough important things to do. I refuse to be a judge on foolish matters of Jewish superstition!"

The Jews were not willing to accept his decision. They pressed their case and refused to leave till judgment was given in their favor. Gallio, who had but lately come from Rome where the Jews were under suspicion, was in no mood to have the beginning of his proconsular year marred in this fashion.

"Drive them out!" he said, turning to the lictors.

Immediately the lictors gave orders to the soldiers to eject them. With drawn swords, the soldiers herded them like cattle from the judgment court.

The Greeks, ever seeking opportunity to taunt the hated Jews, took license from Gallio's attitude to mob them. In the broad open space in front of the entrance to the court of judgment, they grabbed Sosthenes, the ruler of the synagogue, and beat him mercilessly. Others among the Jews were cuffed and kicked. Outnumbered and unprotected by the authorities, the Jews fled and the mob dispersed. Gallio paid no attention to all this, thereby serving notice on the Jews that they should disturb him no more about their religious differences.

This was a significant moment in the career of Paul. It meant that the Christian movement was tolerated by a leading Roman official. The protection of the Empire could be claimed in the future against onsets of the Jews. Paul could stay in Corinth now as long as he liked, so he settled down with determination to make the most of his opportunity. In his imagination he could see the Christian movement flowing from this great crossroads out into every road and byway of the world.

Before long Timothy returned with disturbing news. Paul's teaching while he was at Thessalonica and part of the former letter he had written both focused attention on the hope of Christ's return to the earth, which would bring the end of the world. But false ideas had grown from this teaching, and they distressed Paul greatly. Gladly would he have gone in person to set them straight. But Timothy told him that that was impossible. Before he left Thessalonica, Jason had tried to get the authorities to release him from the bond he had given to keep the peace. The influence of Paul's enemies was too strong, however; and the bond was not lifted. A return of Paul would imperil the whole movement in Thessalonica. His only recourse was to write another letter.

Again Silas took pen in hand to try to transform Paul's heartbeats into words. With characteristic courtesy, Paul began by congratulating the Thessalonians on their steadfastness.

Paul, Silas, and Timothy send greetings to the church of Thessalonica. We feel, brothers, that we owe God a debt of eternal gratitude for the immense loyalty you have shown and for the mutual love which animates each of you. That is why we have been able with pride to draw the attention of all the churches of God to the fortitude and faith you have shown in all the persecutions and afflictions you have endured.

But as to the Second Coming of Christ, Paul had been misunderstood. Someone had deepened the misunderstanding by forging a letter in his name. This must be corrected. The Second Coming was not so near as they thought. They were therefore to keep calm and settled, and to realize that certain conditions had yet to be fulfilled before the end came. He continued to write:

In connection with the coming of our Lord, we ask you not to be easily upset or troubled in your mind. Keep your heads and do not be thrown off balance by any prediction or message or forged letter purporting to come from us, and saying that the day of Christ is almost here. Don't let anyone deceive you by any means whatsoever. There are many decisive battles between good and evil

which must be fought before the end comes. Don't you remember that when I was staying with you I used to tell
you about all this? Therefore, my brothers, stand fast and
keep tight hold of the traditions which you have been
taught both by word of mouth and by our letter. May
our Lord Jesus himself grant you calmness of heart and
strength to perform every kind deed and word.

Some had even gone so far in their mistaken notions of the
nearness of the Second Coming that they had given up their
work, and were sitting idly by waiting for the end. For these
Paul had no sympathy.

Reports are reaching us that there are some of you who
are trifling away your time instead of working. When we
were with you we gave you this principle to work on: "If
a man will not work, he shall not eat." Our order to those
who have abandoned work is to settle down to work and
eat the food they have earned themselves. And the rest of
you—don't get tired of honest work!

I, Paul, add the concluding salutation in my own hand.
That is the assurance of genuineness in every letter we
send. You can tell the writing. Here it is: "The grace of
our Lord Jesus Christ be with you all."

Timothy was dispatched with the letter, and Paul continued
his work in Corinth. He stayed several months more, both to
root out the weaknesses of the rapidly growing church in Corinth and to supervise the work that his helpers were doing in
various centers around Corinth. The church grew both in
numbers and in understanding of the faith, so that Paul's joy
was deep.

But Paul was not one to be content with a measure of success in a local venture. Corinth was but another link in a chain
that he was forging by which he hoped to bind the whole world

to Christ. So, as he preached and instructed and organized in Corinth, he kept his eyes on broader horizons. It was no easy matter to endure the strain of the manifold burdens that he carried daily. A lesser man than Paul would have broken under it.

To light the lamp of truth in Corinth and keep it burning in spite of all the hostile winds that would have blown it out was a herculean task far greater than any ordinary man could have accomplished. But, besides this, Paul carried in his heart and mind countless problems relating to all the other churches he had founded, from which reports came again and again. They were constantly in danger of relapsing into paganism or being misled into legalism by fanatical upholders of the Jewish law. Then, too, he faced the continuing problem of how to keep the Gentile and Jewish Christians together. Furthermore, he was always conscious of the precarious position of the churches with the Roman government, and had to chart a difficult course between compromise with paganism on the one hand and unwise defiance of pagan authorities on the other hand.

A further burden that weighed on Paul was the personal concern he had for so many of his converts who were suffering. His amazing capacity for friendship gave him a very personal interest in all those whom he had brought to Christ, and his unusually sympathetic nature made all their sufferings his. He hungered when they hungered; he bled when they bled; their pain and tears were his also. Little wonder, then, that although he could endure beatings and stonings and personal privations without flinching, there were often tears in his eyes and marks of anguish on his face when his imagination took him on the rounds of his churches. It was no easy matter, either, to determine what his next steps should be. When should he leave Corinth? Where should he go next? What long-range strategy should he carry out in seeking to win the world for Christ?

The only thing that kept Paul going was that he had learned the secret of abiding in Christ, and drawing upon the resources of the One who himself had endured even more than he and had overcome. The living Lord who had met Paul on the road to Damascus had never left him. His life became one long experience of dependence on Christ and of intimate companionship with him. This sense of living in Another was so strong that he wrote to his Galatian friends: "The 'I' that is now living is no longer myself, but Christ who lives in me. The essence of the life that I now live in this world is loyalty to the Son of God who loved me and gave himself for me." Christ's death assured Paul of his never-failing love; his resurrection assured him of his final victory. In the power of these Paul did his work and endured when his own strength would have left him broken under the strain.

After working with unflagging vigor in Corinth for about a year and a half, he began to feel that the time had come when he could safely leave his work there in other hands, and be on his way. He prayed much concerning his next step. Rome was constantly in his mind, and he felt a strong desire to set foot in the world's capital with his gospel. But there was Ephesus, the capital of the province of Asia, where he had hoped to work when his present journey had begun, but from which he had been hindered by the Spirit of Jesus. It seemed unwise to go on to Rome until he had closed in the major gaps behind him. He felt impelled too to make another visit to Jerusalem, in order to report on his work and to try to cement the ties that bound the mother church to the Gentile churches he had founded.

As he pondered his next move in prayer, it seemed best to him to make a journey to Jerusalem, then to return to Ephesus as a next major center of work, after revisiting his other churches in Asia Minor. After a stay in Ephesus, he would go on to Rome. He struck upon a plan of preparing his way in Ephesus by taking Aquila and Priscilla there to work before his return. Accordingly he approached them with his plan.

"I desired to preach in the province of Asia when I began this journey," he told them, "but was hindered. There is not time to do so now on my way to Jerusalem. But I must return at a later time to do it. Come with me now. I will leave you in Ephesus when I pass through on the way to Jerusalem. Establish yourselves there. Your tentmaking can be carried on there as well as here. Prepare the way for my return to Ephesus. I will join you as soon as possible. Ephesus is a strategic center. A church established there can spread the truth in all directions. For the sake of Christ, come!"

Aquila and Priscilla consented. Christ was their life now, not tentmaking, so they were ready to do whatever best served the Kingdom of their Lord. When the news of their leaving was made public, the Corinthian Christians were loath to see these three depart. But sentiment could not stand in the way of the spread of Christ's Kingdom. Amidst prayer, embraces, and not a few tears, Paul, Aquila, and Priscilla broke away from a large group on the shore at Cenchreae, and went aboard ship. Three days on the water, and they cast anchor at Ephesus. There they sought out the synagogue, and made what acquaintance they could among their own people. Paul's message aroused the curiosity of the Ephesian Jews, and they begged him to stay for a while.

"I cannot stay now," he answered. "I will come back to you, if it is the will of God. Meanwhile, these my friends can tell you what I teach."

With that he departed, sailing down the coast in a trading vessel which touched at Cos, Cnidus, and Rhodes, then struck out across the open sea directly to the port of Caesarea, from whence Paul journeyed by land to Jerusalem.

CHAPTER 10

Holding the Line

As Paul journeyed from Jerusalem to Antioch, the marks of inner struggle were on his face. He seemed like a man engaged in heated conversation with himself, utterly oblivious to his surroundings or to events going on around him.

"Every gain has its price," he said to himself. "Each Gentile won to Christ is a wedge driven between me and the Jerusalem church. In becoming a brother to the Gentile, I have become a stranger in my own house."

Any person near him could have heard him muttering to himself: "The Judaizers—Judaizers—will they never cease troubling? They were defeated at the Council of Jerusalem, but they have never given up the struggle."

Paul had good reason to cringe over the Judaizers. In the

years of his absence, these Jewish Christians had turned opinion in Jerusalem increasingly toward their view that it was
necessary for the Gentiles to keep the Jewish law. Although
they had not been able to swing official opinion into line with
their judgment, yet they were able to create an increasing hostility to Paul among the Jerusalem Christians. His visit to
Jerusalem, therefore, had been an unhappy one. To be regarded with suspicion rather than received as a brother was
not what Paul had looked forward to as he came to Jerusalem.

Personal disappointment was deep. But that was not Paul's
chief concern. What matter what happened to him? He had
learned to take personal rebuffs for the sake of his faith. The
thing that stung him deeply was what this was doing to the
church.

"This is making two Churches, not one," he grieved, as he
made his way toward Antioch. "There are Jews who love Jesus. There are Gentiles who love Jesus. But they cannot love
him together. There is one Lord, one faith, one baptism, one
God and Father of us all; yet the family of Christians is not
one! Shall the pagan world, which needs Christ more than
anything else, see two groups of Christ's followers competing,
condemning each other, refusing each other fellowship?"

The prospect of this was intolerable to Paul, and threw a
dark shadow over his spirit.

He had learned in Jerusalem that Peter had gone to Antioch
to investigate reports that the decrees of the Council of Jerusalem were being violated by the Antioch church. Paul wondered what he would find when he arrived there. He was
almost afraid to know, yet he could hardly wait.

Night was falling when he saw in the distance the dim outline of the walls of the city from which he had set out on both
his long missionary journeys. Excitement quickened his pace.
He had not seen his friends there for three years. How had
they fared? What changes had taken place? Had the church
grown? How was Peter's visit turning out? How would Paul

be received? Was their old loyalty to him firm, or had they in
his absence forgotten his leadership and abandoned his teaching? These questions soon would be answered.

A knock, a door swinging open, a strained look into the
darkness to see who had come . . .

"Paul!" exclaimed Symeon, as the apostle moved into the
dim lamplight.

His exclamation brought other members of the household
running to the door.

"You are home at last!" Symeon continued. "You are as welcome as an angel."

Paul sat down to food and drink, while they plied him with
questions about his travels, his health, his work, his friends.

"Rufus! Junias!" Symeon called to his two boys. "Take word
to Lucius and Manaen that Paul is here, and that he is waiting
to see them."

Soon more than a dozen people crowded around Paul in the
home of Symeon, eagerly listening to his rehearsal of his beating and imprisonment at Philippi, his flights from Thessalonica and Berea, his preaching at Athens, and his wonderful success in Corinth.

Before long, however, Paul began to turn the questions toward them. "What has happened in Antioch since I left? Why
is Peter here now?"

It did not take long to tell the story. All had gone well at
Antioch until lately. The Christians, both Jews and Gentiles,
had decided that at their weekly meal in celebration of the
Lord's Supper they would eat together. They were brothers,
worshiping one Lord. Why should they not sit together at a
common table? After news of this reached Jerusalem, Peter
was sent to investigate. When he saw the spirit of unity and
brotherly love that prevailed at these common meals, he approved of their eating together, and joined with them. This
brought angry emissaries from James in Jerusalem. They disputed with Peter, insisting that his behavior, as well as that

of the Jews of Antioch, was a violation of the decrees of the Council of Jerusalem. They pressed their view so vigorously that Peter finally was won over and refused to eat with Gentiles any more. But what was worse, even Barnabas—who had returned from his missionary tour—was carried away by their protests. He who had always championed the cause of freedom for the Gentiles now refused to eat with them.

As these events were retold, Paul said little. But to one who knew him, his response would have been evident. His face grew slightly pale. His eyes took on a piercing cast. The muscles around his mouth tightened.

"But how can this be a violation of the decrees of the Council of Jerusalem?" he finally broke forth. "Those decrees said nothing about Jews eating with Gentiles."

"That is true, Brother Paul," replied Symeon, "and since those decrees freed Gentiles from the Jewish law, we supposed that they had likewise made Jews free to have fellowship with Gentiles. These messengers from James, however, insist that the Jerusalem decrees released Gentiles from the law but did not release Jews from it. Therefore, they contend, it is unlawful for Christian Jews to eat with Christian Gentiles."

This brought to a focus in Paul's mind the problem he had pondered as he journeyed from Jerusalem to Antioch. *Not one Church—but two!* One Father, but two families! One Head, but two bodies!

"We can never submit to such teaching," said Paul. "In Christ there is neither Jew nor Greek; all are one in him. We must settle this question once and for all at any cost!"

At the next meeting of the Christians in Antioch, feeling ran high. Paul publicly confronted Peter with the issue involved. With the ardor of a convinced man, the emotion born of the importance of the question, and native gifts of powerful speech, Paul debated the question boldly, and refused to yield an inch.

"According to the logic of your behavior," Paul insisted to

Peter, "either the Gentiles will have to conform to Jewish eating customs and keep the law or else there will have to be two
Churches. Neither can be tolerated! Forcing Gentiles to conform to Jewish custom was ruled out at the Council of Jerusalem! And there cannot be two Churches of one Christ! If
Jewish Christians in Jerusalem want to keep the law, well and
good. That is as it should be. But where Jews have to mix with
Gentile Christians, they will have to abandon their scruples
in order to maintain unity."

After a lengthy reinforcement of the logic of these convictions, Peter yielded, and harmony was restored to the Antioch
church. They were *one!* They ate, worshiped, and worked together as members of one family.

But it was not enough to win this skirmish at Antioch, and
to bring the Jewish and the Gentile Christians together there.
The Gentile churches and the mother church at Jerusalem
must also be kept together, so that the Church throughout the
world would be one. How could this be achieved? Words
would be less powerful than some practical venture of love.
Paul was shortly to leave on another missionary tour. He determined that he would make it one of the major purposes of
that tour to collect funds among the Gentile churches for the
poor Christians at Jerusalem. Once before he had taken food
to hungry people in Jerusalem when they had looked on him
with suspicion. He would do it again. Sacrificial gifts from
poor Gentiles would cement the ties of love between them and
the Jerusalem Jews in an unbreakable way.

He would begin this by sending a gift with Peter immediately from the Antioch Christians to the Jerusalem church.
This would ease the present tension between the two groups,
for it would convince the Jerusalem Christians that Paul loved
them, even though he differed from them in his views. In the
course of time larger evidence of this love would come from
the Gentile churches in Asia Minor, Macedonia, and Greece.

So, after resting for a period with his friends in Antioch, the veteran traveler set out once more, taking with him Titus, who had lately returned to Antioch after a visit to Galatia.

His destination this time was Ephesus, to which on his former visit he had been asked to return. He was eager to go there because of its strategic location. His former trips had described a large circle, from Antioch through Asia Minor, Macedonia, and Greece, then down to Jerusalem and back to Antioch. Ephesus was almost exactly at the center of that circle. Having formed a ring of Christian churches around the circumference of the circle, he was now ready to work at the center, from which radial lines of influence could go out in all directions.

Ephesus was excellently located to fulfill these plans. It stood near the sea, with which it was connected by a canal and a large artificial harbor, at the head of a long valley which ran into the heart of Asia Minor. The Roman province of Asia was the richest in the Empire, and Ephesus was its capital. Shipping from all ports converged on its harbor, and excellent roads ran to every chief city of the province. Ephesus was a travel center not only because of its commercial interests, but because the Temple of Diana was there, one of the seven wonders of the ancient world. The coming and going of tradesmen and pilgrims formed a constant stream of human traffic to all parts of the Empire. To establish a strong Christian church there would be to send out Christian influences in all directions like the spokes of a wheel from its hub.

It was a journey of several weeks to Ephesus, inasmuch as Paul took occasion to revisit the churches he had formerly founded in central Asia Minor, in the provinces of Galatia and Phrygia. In each city he spent long hours conferring, instructing, exhorting, encouraging. It was his aim so to strengthen these churches that they could survive without further visits from him; then, when he had finished his work at Ephesus, he could move on west toward Rome, to carry Christianity to the capital of the world. Strong emphasis was placed on the systematic collecting of money for the church at Jerusalem as a deep expression of the oneness of the Gentiles and the Jews in Christ. It was strenuous but joyous work—renewing old friendships, uniting in worship, correcting weaknesses and misunderstandings, and building up the faith of the believers in Jesus.

At length he came to Ephesus. Every needle dropped in the tent shop of Aquila when Paul stood in the doorway.

"I knew you would come!" Aquila greeted him. "Not a day has gone by since you left us but we have thought of you and prayed for your return."

All work ceased for the remainder of the day. Paul told nothing of his cold reception at Jerusalem or of his dispute with Peter at Antioch. That would only make a breach which he was anxious to avoid. He reported only the joys of reunion with old friends and the successes of his churches in Galatia and Phrygia.

Aquila and Priscilla too had much to tell Paul and Titus. They had continued to attend the synagogue and had spoken to many in private about Jesus. Then, by a gracious providence, a stranger had arrived—an eloquent teacher from Alexandria—Apollos by name.

"Such speaking we have never heard," broke in Priscilla. "He has a voice like the sound of many waters. Magnificent in physique, and handsome in appearance, he speaks with his whole frame. His words seem to spring out of the deep places of his heart and strike into the deep places of those who hear. He so enthralls one that an hour seems like hardly half its length."

"What is his message?" inquired Paul.

"Now he preaches that Jesus is Messiah," answered Priscilla, "but he did not when he first came. He had heard of John's preaching that the Kingdom is at hand, and that Messiah was soon to come. He sought to persuade the Jews that John was right. When we heard him, we brought him to our home and told him what you had taught us, that Messiah has already come in Jesus. He accepted this and became a powerful preacher of Jesus."

"Why did he not stay?" questioned Paul.

"Visitors from Corinth heard him and insisted that he go with them to preach. We wrote a letter approving his work, and sent him off with them. Reports have come that he has been well received by the church at Corinth."

The conversation then turned to affairs in Ephesus. Aquila and Priscilla had tried to prepare the way for Paul's return. Some of the Jews they had persuaded, but others had expressed opposition. The way was still open for Paul to preach in the synagogue, and he would find quite a group who had already become deeply interested in Jesus.

The first Sabbath after Paul's return found him in the synagogue. He returned again and again, preaching boldly. Many believed; many did not. Opposition at first was courteous and restrained. But gradually it grew in intensity, until some began openly to denounce him in the synagogue services, and to try to persuade the multitudes who came to hear him to close their ears to his message. It soon became apparent to Paul that he could do no effective work in an atmosphere of public dispute. So, after three months, he left the synagogue, hired the lecture hall of a philosopher named Tyrannus, and held daily meetings to which any might come.

The lecture hall was centrally located, so that not only the dwellers at Ephesus but countless travelers from all parts of the world stepped inside to hear Paul teach. His converts became his helpers, and the lecture hall became a hive of continuous activity. Excitement was quickened by the success Paul had in bringing healing to some who were physically and mentally diseased. News of the healings spread rapidly. Anyone who could invoke unseen powers to do the unusual had an immediate hold on the populace of Ephesus. People even became so

convinced of Paul's unusual powers that they would press
through the crowds to try to touch his body with a handker-
chief or an apron which they could carry away to their sick
relatives or friends in the hope of bringing them health.

Public excitement became almost a frenzy through a weird
incident with which Paul had nothing to do. Since Ephesus
abounded in superstition, there were many clever people who
came there to make their living by playing on the fears and
credulity of the masses. Men felt that their lives were determined by fate as truly as the stars were fixed in their courses.
Magic, therefore, became the popular way by which to try to
short-circuit the stars. If, by magical means, the demonic powers of the unseen world could be captured, men hoped that
they could manipulate them to avoid the fixed consequences
of fate. Hence, there were charms for every special purpose and
some that were guaranteed to work for any desired end. But
the demons who helped could also turn and rend one, so there
had to be magical means worked out, after using the power of
a demon, to detach oneself from his interest.

The best means by which one could invoke the power of a
demon, they thought, was to discover and use his name. Since
the demon was eager not to let his name be known, it was well
to utter a vast number of names in the hope of hitting upon
the right one. But once the true name was uttered, results
would be forthcoming; for to have his name was to have control over the one bearing the name.

Since Paul did his work in the name of Jesus, some of the
soothsayers thought that "Jesus" was a magical name of some
demonic power which they too could use to further their trade.
Among these were seven young men, sons of Sceva, a Jew de-
scended from the priestly class. They undertook one day to try
to tame a maniac of whom an evil spirit seemed to have control.

"I adjure you by the Jesus whom Paul preaches," they muttered to the deranged man who had come to their place of busi-

ness. The man had heard of Paul and had heard men speak of Jesus. So he retorted,

"Jesus I know, and Paul I know, but who are you?"

Thereupon, he leaped at them with superhuman fury. Striking, clawing, kicking, biting, he tore the clothes from them, pulled out bits of hair, and sent them fleeing from the building in panic. Down the broad main street of Ephesus he chased them, screaming inarticulate threats and doing his best to overtake them. They outran him to safety, but not before a tremendous crowd had witnessed the whole affair. News of the encounter spread like wildfire. The superstitious populace interpreted this to mean that there was some strange power about the name "Jesus" which only Paul could manipulate, and which others toyed with at their peril.

Daily, therefore, throngs gathered in front of the lecture hall of Tyrannus. They trampled each other to get a glimpse of Paul and to hear him speak. Paul declared emphatically that any powers he had were in no way connected with magic or sorcery—that they were the powers bestowed by Jesus, the Son of the true God and the Saviour of the world. God hated sorcery and all the works of darkness related to it. He was a God of light and life and love, who had created the world and had sent Jesus to redeem it. In the power of the one true God he was doing these works.

Many who had practiced sorcery became converted to Christianity and gave it up. They publicly confessed the charms they had tried to use and the spells they had sought to cast over people for gain. This large-scale abandonment of sorcery in the wake of the excitement over the sons of Sceva had an amazing effect on the city. Converts were added to the church almost too rapidly to give them instruction in the new-found faith. Paul and his helpers were kept busy day and night trying to teach and to mold the lives of those who had cast their lot with Christ. The challenge to sorcery produced opposition, but as yet no open conflict was stirred up. For a time Paul had a taste of unbroken success that surpassed anything he had ever experienced.

One day a traveler arrived in Ephesus. When he was well within the city gates, he accosted a man on the street.

"Friend, can you please direct me to the tentmakers' quarter of the city? I am seeking a tentmaker from Tarsus who is sojourning here in Ephesus for a time. I thought perhaps I might find someone who would know him among those who follow that trade."

"You say your friend is from Tarsus?" queried the man. "What is his name?"

"Oh, he could hardly be identified by his name," the traveler replied. "A hundred men in Ephesus would have the same name. Many a mother names her child Paul."

"Paul!" exclaimed the other. "Paul of Tarsus! You need search no farther. Nearly everybody in Ephesus has heard of him—the teacher of a new religion. He has set the city in an uproar with his strange teachings and his mighty works."

"He visited my town several times—Derbe, in the province of Galatia—and left a deep impression there," answered the traveler.

"You will find him in the lecture hall of Tyrannus. He teaches there every day."

"Could you direct me there?"

"Have you ever been in Ephesus before?"

"No, this is my first visit."

"Well, you can hardly miss it. Just follow this main road until it ends at the circular drive around the bay. Turn to the right along the water front and go through the Forum until you come to another wide road curving back toward the hill. That is the way to the amphitheater. Follow it a few paces, and on the left you will see the school of Tyrannus."

In a half hour, Gaius of Derbe had reached the lecture hall. He stepped quickly inside. Scanning the group hurriedly, and finding every face a strange one, he inquired,

"Is Paul of Tarsus here?"

Before any of them could answer, a youthful figure came bounding through the door from a smaller room, rushed over and threw his arms around Gaius.

"Timothy, my boy," Gaius cried, "how good it is to see you! I have come a long way for this."

"Well, I could hardly have been more surprised had an angel walked in," replied Timothy.

"Is Paul here?"

"Not now. He is working. He refuses to accept support from others lest his enemies accuse him of living by other men's labors. So we support ourselves—tentmaking, you know. While he works, I stay here to teach. When he is here, I work. He should be here soon, however. In the meantime, meet these friends here."

Timothy then introduced Gaius to the others as one of the earliest converts to Christianity in Galatia and as a friend who lived in the town next to his.

"I hope all is well at home," Timothy continued.

"I came through Lystra on my way here and saw both your mother and grandmother. They were well and send their love. They pray for you each day."

"How goes it with the churches?" Timothy inquired.

To this Gaius gave a very evasive answer, which indicated to Timothy that he did not want to discuss the question before the others.

"You are weary from your long journey," Timothy changed the subject. "Come into the other room. There is a couch there where you may rest until Paul comes."

When they were alone, Timothy's curiosity led him to probe Gaius once more for news of the Galatian churches.

"Trouble has arisen, Timothy," Gaius admitted. "I have come to consult Paul. It will perhaps be best if we defer discussion of the difficulties until he arrives."

Gaius then began to ply Timothy with questions about the progress of the work in Ephesus. When Paul had last come through Derbe, he was on his way to Ephesus. Gaius had often wondered what sort of reception he had received.

"God has greatly blessed the work here," Timothy replied. "But the going of late has been rough. As you know, this is the center of the magical arts and the worship of Artemis. The people at first thought that Paul did his mighty works by magic."

Then he told Gaius of the sons of Sceva.

"That had an amazing effect on many. Numbers who had dabbled in the magic arts brought their books of magic and piled them in the street before the lecture hall. Amid the protests of frightened people who thought that it would offend the demonic powers, Paul put a torch to these. Hundreds of people gathered as they burned, holding their breath at what might happen. You should have seen the blaze, Gaius! It witnessed before heaven that worshipers of Jesus have no fear of the unseen powers. He is Lord of Lords.

"And I wish you could have heard Paul preach to the crowd! 'This is done in the name of Jesus!' he told them. 'He has rescued us out of the power of darkness. He is the visible representative of the invisible God. He created the universe. Everything in heaven and on earth, visible and invisible, and all supernatural beings such as thrones, lordships, rulers, and powers—everything was created through him and for him. He is the authority over all authorities, and the Supreme Power over all powers.'

"Then he went on to explain to them, Gaius, that Jesus, in his death and resurrection, had not only wrought personal moral deliverance for individual men, which the mystery religions claimed to do, but he had conquered all the powers of the unseen world and rendered powerless all demonic forces. I never heard Paul rise to such heights in speaking, Gaius, as when he shouted to that immense crowd: 'Christ has drawn the sting of all the powers ranged against us. He exposed them, shattered, empty and defeated, in his final glorious, triumphant act! By his resurrection from the dead he has been given the place of supreme honor in heaven—a place that is infinitely superior to any conceivable command, authority, power, or control, and which carries with it a name far beyond any name that could ever be used in this world or the world to come.'

"His conclusion was overwhelming. It gave the impression of a mighty rushing tide against which nothing could stand. 'I have become absolutely convinced,' he cried, 'that neither death nor life, neither messenger of heaven nor monarch of death, neither what happens today nor what may happen tomorrow, neither a power from on high nor a power from below, nor anything else in God's whole world has any power to separate us from the love of God in Jesus Christ our Lord!'

"Oh, I wish you could have heard Paul preach, Gaius! If I live to be a hundred, I shall never forget those words with which he closed, nor the way I was carried away by the power of Christ that I felt as I heard him.

"The news of this incident spread widely. Visitors to the city were converted and took their new faith back to their homes. Paul has given what counsel he could to all such, and has sent Titus and me and others on visits to various centers to help to raise up the work. All Asia has been stirred. There are churches in Smyrna, Sardis, Philadelphia, Pergamos, Thyatira, Laodicea, and Colossae. The light of Christ is beginning to break through the darkness everywhere, Gaius."

"Has there been no opposition?" asked Gaius, astonished at this lengthy recital of events by Timothy.

"At first there was little. But it has been growing. Both Jews and Greeks are increasing their resistance. The Jews are jealous and afraid. They resent Paul's success, and they fear that if the pagans should turn on him, they would not distinguish between him and them. They have of late, therefore, been throwing every possible obstacle in the way. Paul is an impostor, a deceiver, a fanatic, they say; and they insist that, although he is a Jew by race, he is totally discredited by the rest of the Jews and ought to be silenced."

"And what about the Greeks?" Gaius inquired.

"They feared Paul at first. But now that they see that he is not a sorcerer and intends to do them no harm, they have become increasingly hostile. Christianity is beginning to discredit the worship of Artemis, which is the center of Ephesian life, the thing for which Ephesus is famous. And the business of those who live on superstition is suffering. Feeling is high. Anything may happen. We sometimes fear the worst; but in the meantime the work goes on, and Paul feels that he cannot leave."

At that moment voices of greeting in the outer room indicated Paul's arrival. In an instant Gaius was on his feet. He and Paul embraced. Words seemed useless to express their feeling.

The joy of their greeting did not last long, however. Gaius' story was brief, but it was hard to hear. Some Jewish teachers had come to the Galatian churches, purporting to be sent by the church at Jerusalem, saying that it was necessary for Gentiles to keep the law of Moses in order to be saved. When it was objected that Paul had taught them otherwise, they said that Paul was no apostle. He had not been one of the original Twelve. In fact, he had never seen Jesus at all. He had no standing whatsoever and no authority to teach anything that the apostles in Jerusalem did not teach.

The Galatian Christians had pointed out to them that the apostles in Jerusalem had decreed that it was not necessary for Gentiles to be circumcised to be Christians, and had sent out official word to that effect. The Jewish teachers replied that the decision had been made without sufficient thought and under pressure from Paul. On second thought, the Jerusalem apostles had reversed their decision. As proof of this, they said that Peter had gone to Antioch and, seeing how far they were departing from the law, had withdrawn from all who had not been circumcised. And, what is more, they hinted that even Paul had changed his mind and had gone back on his earlier teaching. The local Jews seized upon these statements and supported the word of the newcomers. Paul's teaching suddenly had been abandoned. The Jews had separated from the Gentiles in the church, and some of the Gentiles had even had themselves circumcised.

As Gaius told this story, Paul sat motionless. When he finished, tears ran down Paul's cheeks.

"My children—" he muttered. "Wolves have torn them to pieces. And the gospel—abandoned!"

He sat looking into space for a long time.

"Have any remained true to me and my gospel?" Paul finally asked, as though he were afraid to hear the answer.

"Would I have come all this way to see you if I had deserted?" replied Gaius. "As long as I live, you will have one loyal friend in Derbe. And at Lystra Timothy's family still stands. And there are others. Antioch and Iconium both have some who have not yielded. All is not lost."

"I will rescue my children from the wolves," said Paul.

"Timothy, go call a scribe. Bring him quickly. I will write a letter to send back with Gaius that will set them straight."

While Timothy was gone in search of a scribe, Paul and Gaius talked at length about the seriousness of the trouble in the Galatian churches. This was no mere matter of Paul's personal authority, nor was it a question of two different interpretations of the Christian faith. It was *truth* that hung in the balance. The very existence of the Christian Church was threatened. The destiny of human souls was involved. Paul's gospel was not his own idea, resting on *his* authority, which men could take or leave as they desired. It was *God's truth,* given to Paul directly by God, which men rejected at the price of rejecting God.

"At any cost, Gaius, we must resist these false teachers," said Paul. "Christ is sufficient for salvation. To impose the religious

customs of us Jews on the Gentiles is to insult God by implying
that his gift of grace in Christ is not sufficient to redeem us.
Furthermore, it will make the church a small sect of Judaism,
when God intends it to include the human race. If these Judaizers succeed in Galatia, they will spread throughout the whole
Church. They must be stopped now. We must insist that the
decision of the Council of Jerusalem has already settled this
issue, and must be regarded as final by everyone."

As Paul talked with Gaius while waiting for Timothy to return, his courage mounted and his letter began to take shape
in his mind.

"This battle is not ours, but Christ's!" he said to Gaius.
"The Christ who in his cross and resurrection has led captive
the raging powers of cosmic evil will not fail in a contest with
a few false teachers in Galatia! The cause is his! The victory is
his! He will triumph!"

Timothy arrived shortly with the scribe, to find Paul pacing
the room like a caged panther. He walked up and down as he
dictated the letter, his eyes blazing and his words coming so
rapidly that the scribe could not keep up. At times his thought
moved faster than his words, and he broke off in the middle of
a sentence to begin another. At other times, he was so stirred
with emotion that tears choked his voice as he spoke. Was it a
letter he was writing? No, it was rather the impossible attempt
to tear out his heart and wrap it up in that parchment to send
back to his Galatian children. He felt so identified with the
cause of Christ that Christ seemed to take over both his feelings and his words. Paul was but an agent of an agonizing love
as deep as that of Gethsemane and Calvary, and the mouth-
piece of truth as glorious and as final as that of the resurrection.

I, Paul, who am appointed and commissioned as special
messenger not by man but by Jesus Christ and God the
Father . . . greeting [he began].

He plunged into the issue immediately, drawing the line clearly between the true gospel and the teaching of those who had been disturbing the Galatian Christians.

I am amazed that you have so quickly transferred to another "gospel"! Not, of course, that it is or ever could be another gospel, but there are obviously men who are upsetting your faith with a travesty of the gospel of Christ. Yet I say that if I, or an angel from heaven, were to preach to you any other gospel than the one you have heard, may he be damned!

He then proceeded to show that his authority for preaching the gospel of God's love in Christ was in no way dependent on his standing with the Jerusalem apostles, for it had come to him directly from God, not from men.

The gospel I preach to you is no human invention. No man gave it to me, no man taught it to me; it came to me as a direct revelation from Jesus Christ. When the time came for God to reveal his Son within me so that I might proclaim him to the non-Jewish world, I did not, as might have been expected, talk over the matter with any human being. I did not even go to Jerusalem to meet those who were special messengers before me. Later, when I went up to Jerusalem to confer with the leaders there, I refused to have Titus circumcised and did not give those who insisted on that an inch, for the truth of the gospel for you and all Gentiles was at stake. And as far as the leaders of the conference were concerned, they had nothing to add to my gospel. Later, when Peter came to Antioch I had to oppose him publicly, for he was then plainly in the wrong when he withdrew and ate separately from the Gentiles out of fear of what the Jews might think.

Common sense should have told them that the gospel

which first brought them release from sin is the gospel in which they should continue.

I will ask you one simple question: Did you receive the Spirit of God by trying to keep the law or by believing the message of the gospel? Surely you can't be so idiotic as to think that a man begins his spiritual life in the Spirit and then completes it by reverting to outward observances? Frankly, you stagger me; you make me wonder if all my efforts over you have been wasted!

When the letter was nearly finished, Paul turned to the scribe.

"Give me the pen," he requested.

He would not allow his enemies to say that this letter was forged and to make sure of this, he would put the final lines in his own handwriting, which they could recognize. This would, in addition, help to strengthen his appeal for personal loyalty.

Look at these huge letters I am making in writing these words to you with my own hand!

These men who are always urging you to be circumcised—what are they after? They want you circumcised so that they may be able to boast about your submission to their ruling. Yet God forbid that I should boast about anything or anybody except the cross of our Lord Jesus Christ. In Christ it is not circumcision or uncircumcision that counts but the power of new birth. To all who live by this principle, to the true Israel of God, may there be peace and mercy!

Let no one interfere with me after this. I carry on my scarred body the marks of my Owner, the Lord Jesus.

The grace of our Lord Jesus Christ, my brothers, be with your spirit.

PAUL.

Paul could not go to Galatia. He never got there again. But as Gaius went off with this letter tucked under his garment, Paul felt that he was sending a little bit of his heart to his Galatian friends—a little of his lifeblood. He was consoled by the belief that they would heed his word and return the love his letter carried. . . . "I carry on my scarred body the marks of my Owner."

CHAPTER 11

Consolidating Gains

Long into the night Paul sat visiting with Titus. He was tormented by a dream—the dream of planting the cross in every great center of the world. What was happening in Ephesus was marvelous. But could that not happen everywhere? And yet— he could not make up his mind what to do. It was useless to plant the cross unless it were rooted deeply enough to stay. Was Ephesus yet ready for him to leave? And what of the churches that had sprung up around it? Would they last without his personal supervision?

He wondered too what was happening in Macedonia and Greece to the churches he had formerly founded there. The bad news from Galatia made him fearful of what might be stirring elsewhere. Then, the poor Christians in Jerusalem—

they needed help. His collection for them must be taken. And he must show them through the gifts he gathered that Jew and Gentile were one in Christ. None of these things could be neglected. What was the next step?

At last he reached a decision. The opportunity in Ephesus was too great to leave at present. Paul would stay, but he would send Titus to Athens and Corinth. Titus could encourage the Christians there, urge them to begin collecting funds for the Jerusalem church, and bring Paul a report of their condition. When Timothy returned from work he was doing in outlying districts near Ephesus, he would send him to make a similar visit to the churches in Macedonia. Then, when Paul was able to leave Ephesus, they would all revisit the churches of Macedonia and Greece, collect the gifts that had been gathered, and take them to Jerusalem. After that—Rome! And then—Spain! The gospel must go to the ends of the earth!

"O God, guide this thy messenger," Paul prayed a few mornings later. "Throw about him the mantle of thy love as he travels. Give him a heart of tenderness for those to whom he goes. Bring him back to me in thy good providence with news that thy Kingdom prospers. For the sake of thy dear Son. Amen."

The two arose from their knees and together walked briskly to the harbor. They stood watching the last bits of cargo being tied in place in the little ship's hold. With an arm on Titus' shoulder, Paul gave him some final words of encouragement and advice. Titus went aboard, the ropes were loosed, the boat rocked gently with the motion of oars maneuvering it away from the dock, across the bay, and into the canal which led four miles to the open sea. Paul stood on the shore watching, and waved a last farewell just as the boat rounded a bend in the canal and disappeared from sight.

Five weeks later Titus returned. He brought not only a report, but a friend. Paul recognized him immediately from the description others had given of him. Tall, dark, graceful of motion, with penetrating eyes—who could it be but Apollos? It was interesting to see Paul and Apollos together. Apollos was smooth of speech, gracious in manner, still in the bloom of youth, a little overawed in the presence of one so great as the apostle. Paul was more abrupt in speech, a little awkward in manner, prematurely aged by his hardships, but with a mind that worked fully twice as fast as that of Apollos, and a self-forgetfulness that made him at ease and unconscious of his own less commanding presence.

The news from Corinth was not good. Apollos had had some success in winning other converts there, but immorality had broken out in the church. Paul had preached that Christians were free from the law. Some took this to mean that they were free of all moral restraint. The offenders were ecstatic people who often worked themselves up into an emotional frenzy and spoke with strange tongues. When Apollos upbraided them for their immorality, they always justified it on two grounds: First, Paul had taught them they were free from the law. To object to their behavior was to put them back under the law. Secondly, since speaking with tongues was a gift of the Holy Spirit, it was evident that God approved of them. Unable to halt this unfortunate behavior, Apollos had decided to return to Ephesus with Titus.

Paul immediately wrote a letter to the church at Corinth. They had misunderstood his teaching, he told them. They were free from the law, but free to do good, not evil. And their character should reflect the character of the holy God who had freed them from the law.

There can be nothing in common between righteousness and lawlessness any more than between light and darkness. What agreement can there be between Christ and the devil? Therefore, let us keep clear of anything that smirches body or soul. Let us prove our reverence for God by consecrating ourselves to him completely.

He advised them, therefore, to separate themselves from all fellowship with those who were immoral in their behavior. The letter was sent by Titus, who returned with the report that the friends of Paul had been encouraged by this clarification of his teaching. They now had Paul's authority to use against those who were immoral. Paul breathed easier over the situation at Corinth, and threw himself again into the work at Ephesus.

Weeks went by. Time can heal, but time can also hurt. If only Paul could have seen what was happening at Corinth! Finally the news reached him. There arrived at the school of Tyrannus three friends from Corinth.

"Stephanas!" Paul cried in surprise. "And Fortunatus! And Achaicus!" He tried to throw his arms around all three of them as he spoke. "It is like the coming of a breeze on a hot night to see you. What brings you? Good news, I hope?"

"Our news is not good," replied Stephanas. "We have come for help. We bring you a letter from the church at Corinth, seeking your judgment on some matters in dispute." With that he handed some small, square sheets of papyrus to Paul.

Paul was not long in reading. A dispute had arisen concerning his teaching on two points. They were writing to him to settle it. What were his teachings on marriage, and was it lawful to eat meat that had been offered to an idol by a pagan priest before being sold on the market?

"Is this all the trouble at Corinth?" Paul inquired, as he laid the letter down. He almost feared to hear the answer, for some servants of a well-to-do Christian lady in Ephesus had but lately returned from a visit to Corinth, telling Paul that deep divisions had arisen in the church there. Of the reasons they were not sure.

"I wish that *were* all," replied Stephanas. "These are minor difficulties and do not touch the heart of the matter. Trouble began with those of immoral behavior. We had hoped that your former letter would settle that. The guilty parties, how-

ever, wrongly interpreted it, insisting that your advice to separate from fornicators could not be kept without going completely out of this world. Our objections to their behavior,
therefore, have been without avail and immorality has increased."

"Why do you not take drastic action and exclude them from
the Christian fellowship?" Paul asked.

"Because we are divided into factions, and have quarreled
over the question of whose authority to follow."

At this point, Fortunatus took up the story.

"The question might have been handled had it not been for
the arrival of some Jewish Christians from Jerusalem."

On hearing this, Paul visibly winced. *Jewish Christians from
Jerusalem!* What they had done in Galatia came to mind! Had
they gone as far as Corinth? Paul was prepared to hear almost
anything now.

"When we proposed to seek your advice," Fortunatus con-

tinued, "they objected on the ground that you had no authority as an apostle. You had been effective, they admitted, as a
preacher, but authority to settle disputes was not yours but
Peter's. They insisted that it was your preaching of freedom
from the law that had caused the dispute, and that only Peter
could settle it."

"How do matters stand now?" Paul asked.

Achaicus spoke up in reply. "Since we could not agree on
who had authority to handle matters, the situation has gone
from bad to worse. Some of us are still loyal to you. Others,
gripped by the preaching of Apollos, feel that he ought to settle
the dispute. The Jerusalem group have rallied a large following who are holding out for Peter's authority. Meanwhile, the
immoral offenders, who call themselves the party 'of Christ,'
have grown more bold in their behavior. The church is hopelessly split into factions. Some of the Christians have taken
their personal grievances for settlement to pagan law courts.
Disorder and bickering have intruded even into the observance of the Lord's Supper. Those who speak with tongues and
claim special spiritual gifts have lorded it over others. We need
help, Paul! We need it badly, and we need it quickly!"

As Paul listened to this recital of the unfortunate situation
at Corinth, he wondered what he ought to do. Should he answer their letter by another letter, or go in person? A visit to
Corinth had been in his mind for a good while, but he did not
want to leave Ephesus until the work there was established.
Just recently he had been getting an unusual response to his
preaching. He felt that he could not leave yet. He must at least
stay until the next annual Feast of Artemis, when great crowds
would pour into the city. A letter sent back with these emissaries from the church of Corinth would have to do for the
present. Meanwhile, he would request Timothy, who was just
on the point of leaving for Macedonia, to extend his journey
and visit Corinth to reinforce the effect of the letter. Then,
immediately after the Feast of Artemis, he would go in person.

If the Corinthians knew he was coming shortly, his letter and
Timothy's visit should tide them over until he arrived.

He sent for a scribe and began:

From Paul, divinely appointed apostle of Jesus Christ.

Then, after some introductory remarks, he launched into
the problems the Corinthians were facing.

I beseech you, brothers, in the name of our Lord Jesus
Christ, to avoid dissensions. Chloe's people have reported
to me that you are divided into cliques. One of you says,
"I follow Paul"; and another, "I follow Apollos"; and
another, "I follow Peter"; and another, "I follow Christ."
Is then Christ divided? Was Paul crucified for you? After
all, who is Paul, and who is Apollos? Just ministers by
whose means you were brought to conversion. You don't
belong to those leaders of whom you speak, but they belong to you. And you belong to Christ as Christ belongs
to God.

He then inserted an appeal for personal loyalty, hoping that
inasmuch as he was one of the leaders over whom the Corinthians were quarreling, his appeal for peace might be effective.

I am not writing this to put you in the wrong, but I am
trying to advise you as if you were my own dear children.
You may have thousands of teachers in Christ, but you
haven't many fathers. It was I who was actually responsible for your birth in the gospel through Christ Jesus.
Won't you then try to imitate me as children imitate their
father? That is the reason why I have sent Timothy to
you. He is my dear faithful son in the Lord and he will
remind you of the way in which I tried to order my life

after the pattern of Christ. But I shall come in person, and very soon, if God wills; and then I shall find out what these self-satisfied people are worth, not in verbosity, but in effectiveness. The Kingdom of God is not established by argument, but by effective action. Which would you prefer, that I come to you with a big stick or in love and gentleness?

Following that, Paul launched into other problems facing the church at Corinth—immorality, lawsuits, irresponsible living, marriage, food offered to idols, fanaticism.

There is rumor that among you there has actually been committed incest. I wrote to you in my last letter not to associate with immoral persons. I did not mean that you could avoid all contact with such people. To do that you would have to leave the world altogether. It is no business of mine to pass judgment on non-Christians. Those who are outside must be left to God's judgment. But as to any of our own brethren who has been convicted as immoral, lustful, idolatrous, abusive, drunken, or as a robber, as I wrote before, "The evil person must be expelled from your company."

When you have a case against another member of the Church, how dare you take it before a pagan court? Why not rather suffer wrong?

There are some who claim that as Christians they have a right to do anything. "To us," they say, "everything is lawful." Don't you know that your body is the shrine of the Holy Spirit? You do not belong to yourselves; you have been bought at a price. Then honor God in your body.

Now to touch on the points about which you wrote.

You ask whether the unmarried state is not the best condition of life. My answer is that in order to avoid immorality it is better for each man to have a wife of his own and for each woman to have a husband.

Regarding now the question of eating food which has been sacrificed to idols: we know that an idol is really nothing at all, and that actually there is only one God. However, not everyone possesses this knowledge, and for him to eat food offered to idols would put a burden on his conscience. It would be terrible for your knowledge to destroy the weak, especially when you remember that he is a brother for whom Christ died. So if the eating of such meat is a source of offense to my brother, rather than offend him I will become a vegetarian for as long as I live.

As to special spiritual gifts (such as speaking with tongues, special visions, the ability to preach eloquently), supposing I could speak in ecstasy with the languages of all the different races of men and even with those of the different orders of angels; even though I were a prophet and could penetrate every mystery; even though I had all faith so that I could remove mountains, and had not love, I should be nothing. First make sure of love, therefore, which lasts forever, and then try for spiritual gifts.

Perhaps the most serious problem the Corinthians were facing—more serious even than their quarreling and immorality—was the disbelief of some of them in the resurrection. The Christian faith was strong enough to heal their quarrels and overcome their immoral living in time. But if the resurrection were untrue, then there was no such thing as the Christian faith, for it rested squarely on the resurrection of Jesus from the dead. Paul saw this with clarity. His own conversion to Christianity had come through meeting the risen Lord. If Christ were not raised, then he had been living on one grand illusion, and both his personal faith and the work of a whole lifetime counted for nothing. He, therefore, drove this point home in his letter with great force.

Some of you say there is no such thing as a resurrection of the dead. If there is no resurrection of the dead, then Christ was not raised. But if Christ was not raised, then there is nothing real in our preaching or in your faith. However, we know that Christ has been raised from the dead. "Death is swallowed up in victory." O death, where is now your victory, and where, O death, your sting? Thanks be to God, who through our Lord Jesus Christ, has bestowed on us the victory.

The letter closed with an appeal for generosity in collecting money for the church in Jerusalem, and with an account of Paul's personal plans.

It was not long after this letter was dispatched that Stephanas hurriedly returned to tell Paul that it had been ill received and had made matters worse instead of better.

"It's terrible, Paul," he confided. "The Libertines are saying all sorts of things: You don't know what the gospel is. Your letters are strong, but you are a weakling face to face. It is none of your business what they do with their money. You refused financial help before just to fool them, so that you can help yourself to the money you are now raising for the poor at Jerusalem. I've never heard such vicious attacks, Paul, by anyone who claimed to be respectable."

"How did the Jewish party respond?" Paul inquired.

"Less viciously than the Libertines, but none too well. They say you are trying to use authority you do not have. The fact that you took no money on your first visit, they say, proves that you had some doubts yourself of your position. Furthermore, they have letters of commendation from Jerusalem, which you do not have. They still insist that authority resides in Peter and the Jerusalem apostles."

It was evident as Stephanas spoke that Paul was undergoing an inner struggle. Hardly had he finished when a look of determination suggested that Paul's decision had been made.

"Stephanas, I am grateful to you for telling me what has caused you pain to talk about," Paul said. "It has pained me more to hear it. But the situation must be faced. The cause is not mine, but Christ's. I will return to Corinth with you to straighten out this trouble. The trip will not take long. I can get there and back before the great festival of Artemis. I can leave Titus in charge here while I am gone. Come, we must make immediate arrangements for sailing."

The two had opportunity to discuss the whole question at length during the two days of their trip. In the light of all that Stephanas had to tell, Paul laid his plans and decided on the best method of procedure when he reached Corinth.

The emotional tension produced by weeks of bickering was extremely high among the Corinthian Christians. When Paul arrived, he was snubbed ruthlessly by many who had been converted under his preaching, and received coldly by all except a few who had remained immovably loyal to him. These, fortunately, were the strongest in character and the most level-headed in judgment. But the Libertines and the Jewish party were in no mood to be reasoned with, so that Paul's friends could do nothing to bring them into line.

Paul met with the whole Christian group at the house of Titus Justus. He spoke directly to the issues at stake, and with passionate eloquence sought to set them in a new light.

"These problems are not to be solved on the level of human quarreling," he insisted. "We must remember that we Christians belong to Christ, and can solve our problems only as we face them in the Spirit of Christ. While there are jealousies and quarrels among you, are you not still worldly, and is not your behavior just on the human level? When one says, 'I belong to Paul's party,' and another says, 'I follow Apollos,' are not you behaving like mere worldlings?"

His enemies, however, misinterpreted this effort, and said that he was trying to hide the real problem of his own authority behind pious words about the Spirit of Christ. Whereupon, a general scene of confusion broke out, which Paul had often experienced in synagogues where his word was not believed, but which he had never before seen in a Christian gathering. He tried in vain to quiet them and to reason with them. They heckled him, ridiculed him, and drowned out his voice so that it was impossible for him to speak further.

Finally, the climax was reached in a personal insult. One of the party that had been insisting that it made little difference what they did since Christ had freed them from the law strode to the front of the group. Taking hold of Paul's arm, he insinuated that Paul did not believe his own teaching, but was merely insisting on upright morals as a cloak for his own unworthy behavior in secret. Paul could take much, but this he could not endure. He was Christ's ambassador. To insult him in that fashion was an affront to Jesus Christ.

For a moment Paul fastened his gaze on him. His eyes blazed as though they would scorch his enemy's skin. Then suddenly, with a jerk, he broke loose from the grip of his accuser, strode briskly to the corner of the room where he had laid his outer garments, picked them up, and walked out of the house. He headed straight for the docks to find passage back to Ephesus.

A few of his friends followed him to the docks. They did the best they could to apologize, but explained that he had been given a bitter taste of the sort of thing they had been up against ever since the controversy broke out. Paul let them know that he held them in no way responsible, but that in protest against such behavior he would have to leave. He was stung to the core, and was in no mood to converse at length. The hour was late. There was a boat he could board sailing for Ephesus before daybreak. Paul, therefore, dismissed his friends to their homes against their prolonged protests, and curled up on a rough mattress on the deck of the little ship to sleep—no, not to sleep! To endure the nightlong agony of a father whose children had cursed him!

As Paul sat for two days watching the gentle spray thrown

up by the prow of the boat, he was greatly perplexed as to his next move. The issue was serious. If the breach were not healed, it would mean the breakup of the largest church he had founded. This then might affect his other churches and lead to the dissolution of much of his life's work. If this should happen, the plans Paul had for a large offering for the church at Jerusalem would be wrecked. The report of his differences at Corinth with the emissaries from Jerusalem would widen the breach already existing between Paul's churches and the Jerusalem church. If now the offering failed, that would be the final blow. The hopes of a lifetime were balancing on the edge of ruin.

But Paul was not a quitter. Upon reaching Ephesus he decided—much against the judgment of Titus—to make one last desperate effort to set things right at Corinth. He would write another letter, a severe letter, containing an ultimatum. Either the Corinthian church must expel the offending members or Paul would make another visit and cast them out himself. Paul wrote this letter with inner torment. He was tossed back and forth between hope and fear—hope that his severe reprimand would bring the Corinthian church to its senses and save the day, and fear that it would fail. Love too added its pangs; for in rebuking the Corinthians he was scourging his own children, for whom he would gladly have given his life. His words seemed like putting salt in open sores. His heart was wrung with agony, and he wept much as he wrote. Titus was appointed to deliver the letter, to stay in Corinth for a time in order to add the weight of his personal influence to that of Paul's friends, and to bring Paul a report of the outcome. By that time Paul intended to leave Ephesus himself for a visit to Macedonia. Titus, therefore, was to meet him in Troas. If his report were good, Paul would make his visit to Macedonia and then go on to Corinth. If the report were bad, he would go directly to Corinth from Troas. With a good deal of doubt as to the outcome, Titus took his leave.

After his departure, Paul redoubled his efforts to organize his work in Ephesus so that it would go forward in his absence. Already pilgrims from distant places were arriving for the annual festival to the goddess Artemis, called by the Romans Diana. Paul planned to stay until this was over, for any influence that his work might have on that occasion would spread to every city or village from which the travelers had come.

Twice before, Paul had witnessed the great spectacle which was famed throughout the Empire. It centered in the Temple of Artemis, built about a mile out of the city. The old temple, which Croesus had dedicated, had burned to the ground on the night in which Alexander the Great was born, in the year 356 B.C. Contributions to the rebuilding of the temple were made by the whole of Asia. It took more than two hundred years to complete it. A forest of columns—one hundred and twenty-seven of them—each sixty feet high, each cut in one piece out of solid marble, graced the exterior of the building. Its interior

was beautified with cyprus and ivory, and it housed dozens of the finest pieces of Greek art in existence.

The central attraction was a crude image of the Asiatic goddess Artemis, which legend said had dropped out of the heavens. She was the goddess of fertility, symbolizing nature, out of which all life comes. Attendant upon the goddess were dozens of priests and priestesses, who directed ceremonies of worship which were degraded into sexual orgies. The temple and the sacred precincts around it were filled with thousands of little shrines, which were bought by the masses and dedicated to the goddess. Made of silver, or marble, or terra cotta, patterned after the temple with the goddess inside, these offerings were so innumerable that the priests had to clear them away frequently to make room for new ones.

The temple was also a depository of money, in which the funds both of the city and of private citizens were kept. Furthermore, no arrests of criminals were permitted within arrow shot of the temple. It became, therefore, the hangout of the criminal class, who had fled there for immunity from the law. Their presence helped to degrade the moral tone of the temple worship. Priests, temple harlots, criminals, crowds of pilgrims —the human actors at the scene were as depraved as the temple was magnificent.

A fine boulevard, running from the east gate of Ephesus to the entrance of the sanctuary, connected the temple with the city. Two thoroughfares for vehicles, with a walkway for pedestrians between them, made the flow of traffic easy and safe. Countless statues lined both sides of the roadway, making the entire mile almost like a corridor of a gallery of rare works of art. At the annual festival, a long procession paraded down this thoroughfare from the temple to the city. Dancing girls led the way, scattering flowers along the boulevard. They were followed by priests in leopard skins, some preceding and some following a float on which were carried costly statues of the goddess, donated to the city by a wealthy Roman. Then came the main float, bearing a golden image of the goddess. Musicians were next in procession, after whom came a woman dressed as a divine huntress with bow and quiver. The procession ended with a long line of animals, led on leashes, representing the world of nature, of which Artemis was the mother goddess. Young men in holiday attire met the procession at the city gate and led the way into the great stadium. There the celebration ended, as the crowd broke up and returned to the temple to complete the scene with riotous orgies.

It was for the return of this occasion that Paul was waiting. As soon as it was over, he planned to leave for Troas and Macedonia. His departure was hastened, however, in a way he had not expected. The clash of Christianity with superstition and magic was beginning to make itself felt in an economic way. The tradesmen who earned their living by making the shrines dedicated to the goddess at the temple, which were carried home by every pilgrim to the sacred shrine, found their business falling off noticeably. A new wave of conversions, just at the time of the annual festival during which their business was normally at its peak, convinced them that if the Christian movement were not checked, their livelihood would be seriously threatened.

The head of the guild of silversmiths, named Demetrius, called a meeting of the guild, to which he invited all tradesmen whose work was in any way related to the art of magic or the worship of Artemis. When they were assembled at the guild house, Demetrius addressed them:

"Men, you know that from this business of making objects of devotion we have our wealth. And you see and hear that not only at Ephesus but almost throughout all Asia this Paul has persuaded and turned away a considerable company of people saying that gods made with hands are not gods. And there is danger not only that this trade of ours may come into disrepute but also that the temple of the great goddess Artemis may count for nothing, and that she may even be deposed from her magnificence, she whom all Asia and the world worship."

On hearing this, the crowd of workmen broke into a frenzy. Paul had touched two things that came very close home—their pocketbooks and their religion.

"Where is the atheist?" someone called out. "Drag him out into the theater, where he may be tried and condemned!"

"Great is Artemis of the Ephesians!" others clamored.

In a mighty rage they rushed as one man out of the guildhall into the street, and began a march to the amphitheater. As they rushed along, their number grew. Every passer-by, curious to know what was going on, joined the mob. The shouting increased into a roar that was deafening.

"There's one of them!" cried one of the leaders as he rushed over and grabbed a man named Gaius. "He's a friend of this Paul!"

"Are you one of them too?" yelled another, as he laid hold of Aristarchus, who was walking with Gaius. Before Aristarchus could answer, he was whisked into the whirling mob and dragged along.

The procession surged into the great amphitheater. The roar of their shouting could be heard throughout the city. Men left their work, women their homes, and children their play to rush to the scene to see what was happening. Most of them had not the slightest idea of what was going on, but they were caught in the hysteria of the mob and joined their voices with the others in yelling.

Some of the Jews of the city discovered the cause of the trouble, and began to fear that since Paul was a Jew the mob would not distinguish between the Christian movement and Judaism. This might mean that they would be innocently caught in a wave of persecution. Hoping to avoid this, they pushed Alexander, one of their leading men, up onto the great platform near one end of the amphitheater to speak to the crowd. He raised his hand for silence, but when the mob saw that he was a Jew, their violence was quickened by their customary hatred of the Jews. All Alexander succeeded in doing was to heighten the passion of the crowd.

For two hours the roar of the mob was unabated. Confusion reigned. No one could make out anything except that now and again the chant: "Great is Artemis of the Ephesians! Great is Artemis of the Ephesians!" could be distinguished.

Not long after the sound of the mob reached Paul's ears at the home of Aquila where he was staying, the door burst open and a teen-age youth rushed in, white and trembling.

"They're after us!" he cried. "They're going to get us!"

"After whom?" Paul inquired.

"Us Christians!" the lad replied. "I heard some of them say that they would kill every Christian in the city!"

"Do not be afraid, my boy," said Paul, placing his hand on the boy's shoulder and drawing him reassuringly to himself. "God will take care of us. I will go and speak to the mob."

"No, Paul," spoke up Aquila. "Mobs do wild things. It is not well to risk yourself foolishly."

But Paul would not listen. He set out for the amphitheater. Aquila, unable to dissuade him, went with him. The school of Tyrannus was not far from the amphitheater. Others of the Christian group would be there. Aquila, therefore, insisted that Paul go to the lecture hall first and consult with the other Christian brothers. This he consented to do, but still with the determination that he would enter the great amphitheater and speak to the mob. It held nearly twenty-four thousand people, and it must have been nearly full by this time. When would he ever have such an opportunity to preach in Ephesus again!

When he arrived at the lecture hall, several of the brothers were there. They all refused to permit Paul to venture forth, fearing for his life. Just then word arrived by messenger from the Asiarchs, the Roman officials who presided over the religious festivals and had charge of the imperial religion, that it would be very unwise for Paul to risk himself before the mob. This finally dissuaded Paul from his purpose, and he reluctantly gave up his hope of preaching to the vast throng.

At long last, the clerk of the city got the mob quieted down enough to speak to them. He was deeply concerned over the possible consequences of this riot to the city. Ephesus was allowed a good deal of independence by the Roman proconsul, and matters pertaining to the life of the city that did not run counter to Roman law could be settled by a popular assembly. These assemblies could not be called, however, except with the permission of the proconsul. Since the present gathering was thus illegal, it might involve the city in disciplinary action which would curtail their freedom, so that this example of illegal assemblies would not spread to other centers. Hence, the clerk addressed the mob:

"Men of Ephesus, what man is there who does not know that the city of the Ephesians is temple keeper of the great Artemis, and of the sacred stone that fell from the sky? Seeing then that these things cannot be contradicted, you ought to be quiet and do nothing rash. For you have brought these men here who are neither sacrilegious nor blasphemers of our goddess. If therefore Demetrius and the craftsmen with him have a complaint against anyone, the courts are open, and there are proconsuls; let them bring charges against one another. But if you seek anything further, it shall be settled in the regular assembly. For we are in danger of being charged with rioting today, there being no cause that we can give to justify the commotion."

With these words, he bade the mob disperse and return in quietness to their homes.

This was all a new experience for Paul. Heretofore, his persecutions had usually taken their rise in Jewish hostility. Now, for the first time, the Christian faith had run squarely up against the pagan world. What would the future hold? Paul saw that such clashes would be more frequent as the Christian movement grew. Would the Roman government tolerate Christianity and protect Christians from pagan mobs? Or would it turn against it and persecute it? Paul had faced this question before in his own mind. Now it was sharpened by these events. He reflected long on the possible outcome.

It seemed wise for Paul to move on from Ephesus and not to put the question to an immediate test. Although the present danger was past, his presence in the city might incite Demetrius and his group to further riot. Paul felt that he ought not to involve the other Christians in difficulty by the personal hatred Demetrius had for him. So, calling the Christian group together for a farewell meeting, and encouraging them to continue in the way of faith, he took leave of them and departed for Troas.

At Troas, Paul was to wait for Titus to return from Corinth. Desiring never to miss an opportunity to spread Christianity, he undertook, while waiting for Titus, to preach in Troas. He had some success, and gathered a little Christian group around him. But he was restless and greatly disturbed. The accumulated problems of a lifetime seemed to be concentrated at that point in his career. He had been through many depressing experiences with regard to a single situation, but now all the strands he had been weaving through the years seemed to be tangled, and he was caught in the midst of them.

Day after day Paul went to the wharf to inquire whether there was any news of a ship's approach from Macedonia or Achaia. Day after day he was disappointed.

"Will Titus never come?" he asked himself again and again. "What has happened in Corinth that he is delayed? If my letter and his visit have failed, how can I face it? Another visit to Corinth to handle that nasty situation will be more than I can bear."

He could not forget the work he had left behind, either, nor the fate of the distant churches he had not visited for a long time. He had been gone from Ephesus for a very short time— hardly long enough for any changes to have taken place— yet it seemed longer to Paul and, like a mother sending her child forth on his own for the first time, he feared the worst.

"I wonder how the brothers in Ephesus are standing since I left?" he asked himself. "Are Demetrius and his followers molesting them? Do they have courage and wisdom, if the worst should come? Will their old superstitions revive in my absence and the church be engulfed in paganism? And what is happening in Galatia? If only I could hear how my letter there was received! And the offering for the church in Jerusalem— will that be a success? Suppose I find that the Gentile churches have raised but a pittance? How can I take that down to Jerusalem as a token of their love, and a bond to unite Jew and Gentile? I wonder too how much news has traveled back to Jerusalem about the trouble I have had in my Gentile churches? If they have heard, it is sure to be exaggerated and misinterpreted. That would mean the end of my hopes for one Church."

Questions like these distracted Paul daily. He was alone; and when he was alone for long, he was never at his best. With no news, the path back from the docks seemed harder to walk each day. Disappointment, frustration, fearful imaginings—how could he stand it longer!

Finally, in desperation, he decided not to wait for Titus, but to go to Macedonia to try to intercept him there. So he said farewell to his new friends at Troas, boarded ship, and crossed the sea to Philippi. What a reunion! Lydia, the jailer, the sorceress whom he had cured, and Luke, and Timothy, who had just returned to Philippi! These and others took him to their hearts with a warmth that cheered him deeply. His spirit immediately began to revive. He was greatly heartened by the progress of the church in Philippi. New converts had been added, and the older ones had grown into Christian maturity. To climax the good news, Titus arrived shortly with excellent news from Corinth. The insult to Paul on his last visit there had shown the better element of the Corinthian church how low the Libertines would stoop and how devoid of Christian

grace their spirit was. This had rallied the loyalties of the better members to Paul. They had dealt effectively with the Lib-
ertine offenders, many of whom had repented. Order had been
restored, fellowship re-established, and the Corinthians were
eagerly awaiting a visit from Paul.

Immediately, Paul sat down and wrote a fourth letter to the
Corinthian Christians, expressing his gratitude at Titus' good
report, his joy that they had set things right, and his anticipa-
tion of a joyous visit to them instead of a grievous one. He also
encouraged them by the example of the Macedonian churches
to work hard on the collection, so that when he came a goodly
amount would be ready to carry to Jerusalem as a visible bond
of their oneness with the Jewish Christians. After dispatching
the letter, Paul made a tour of the churches of Macedonia.
Then he went to Attica, spending some time in Athens, and
finally arriving in Corinth. Three months were spent there in
glad fellowship, the old troubles having been healed.

Two things were on Paul's mind now: first, he must get the
offering safely to Jerusalem; then he would make his long-
anticipated journey to Rome. Paul's vision of taking the whole
world for Christ made Rome bulk large in his mind. Not only
all roads, but all the avenues of the mind and heart converged
on Rome. It was the heart of a colossal empire, to which philosophy, art, commerce, and religion constantly flowed, to be
pumped out again to the ends of the earth with the stamp of
the imperial city on it. To take Christ to Rome! What a prospect! To transfuse into the lifeblood of that vast city the Spirit
of Christ would mean to send the Christian faith through all
the arteries of life to the borders of the world!

Paul would have liked to be the first one to preach in Rome.
It was his custom to spend his efforts on centers where Christ
was not known—to pioneer in the difficult places rather than to
fulfill the easier task of building on foundations that someone
else had laid. But the gospel had gone to Rome long before he
could get there. Countless Christian travelers spoke to him

often of the church in Rome. Many of his own converts had made their way to the imperial city to live, and were now members of the church there. He felt, therefore, that he was really acquainted with the church there even though he had never set foot in the city, and he wanted to have some part in spreading the influence of Christ where human power was at its height.

There was a strong Jewish colony in Rome, so that the church there was made up of both Jews and Gentiles. From reports that had come to him, Paul knew that the Roman church was facing the same problem that his own churches had faced with regard to Jewish-Gentile relations. In order, therefore, to help with a solution to this difficulty before he reached Rome, and also to send the Christians there a cordial greeting before he visited them, he sat down to write them a letter.

Because he was writing to people to whom he had never preached, he decided to lay before them the whole outline of the gospel he proclaimed, and to deal with the specific question of Jewish-Gentile relations in the church as a part of the broad fabric of his whole teaching. So, calmly and deliberately, with keen logic and guarded reasoning, he worked out in his letter the thoughts he had flung off in the heat of conflict in his letter to the Galatians.

The background of all Paul's thinking lay in the character of God as revealed in the Scriptures and confirmed by Jesus. God is utterly holy, a blazing flame of moral perfection, before whom nothing evil can stand. All men have sinned against this holy God. The pagan has sinned by acting against the universal moral law written in his conscience. The Jew is no better, for he has sinned against the righteous demands of God as set forth in the law of Moses. What then? Both pagan and Jew stand condemned before a holy God.

How, then, can men be saved? How can they hope to be on good terms with God in this life, and share his eternal life in the world to come? Certainly not by anything that they can do themselves. For none of our doings can undo our past wrongs. Furthermore, when we judge our doings in the light of God's moral perfection, our best deeds are tainted with self-interest, and are therefore quite worthless in themselves, to say nothing of having any merit in overcoming our past wrongs.

Is there any solution to man's dilemma? Yes, God's solution. God is holy, but he is infinitely merciful. He has come to earth in the Person of Jesus, who as representative man has voluntarily taken into his own life the consequences of our wrongdoing, and replaced our evil with his perfect doing of God's will. Salvation, then, is not something that we can achieve by our own efforts. It is rather something that God has achieved for us in the life, death, and resurrection of Jesus. He now offers salvation to us as a free gift. Faith is nothing other than believing this and accepting God's gracious gift of forgiveness. This brings to the one who believes peace with God, deliverance from sin, and power to lead a new life. Paul followed his long statement of his gospel with a description of the high type of life those who have been redeemed ought to live.

In this way Paul showed that there is one God of all men; that all have sinned—both Gentile and Jew; and that all are redeemed by Christ. Among those who accept this redemption, therefore, there can be neither Jew nor Greek. The Church is one fellowship of men of all races and conditions in life, who live by faith, who labor in love, in the patience of hope.

Rome! Paul had never seen Rome, nor had Rome ever seen him. But when the Roman Christians read this letter, they knew immediately that the one who was announcing a coming visit was no ordinary man! And from then on until Paul arrived in the imperial city, his visit was eagerly awaited.

After sending off the Roman letter with a trusted Christian friend, Phoebe, a deaconess of the church at Cenchreae, who was on her way to Rome, Paul carefully laid his plans for conveying the offering to Jerusalem. Delegates had been appointed from Galatia, Asia, and Macedonia to accompany Paul with their share of the offering. They all gathered at Corinth at the appointed time to sail from there together. Passage was booked on a ship taking Jewish pilgrims to the Feast of the Passover. They were about to go on board, when—suddenly—news of a secret plot on Paul's life came to light! The Jews who had unsuccessfully tried to get Gallio to condemn Paul on his first visit to Corinth had decided to take justice into their own hands. Assassins had been appointed to sail on the same boat with Paul to murder him!

Neither Jerusalem nor Rome would have seen Paul had this plot not come to light. But God was not yet through with Paul. His companions went on board as planned. But Paul himself left Corinth secretly by land, to elude his assassins.

PART FOUR

The Triumph

CHAPTER 12

Gathering Storm

T HE NIGHT AIR was cool. There was little to break the silence but the steady rhythm of sandaled feet on the road.

"Their hatred is deeper than I thought," Paul finally spoke.

"It was a close call," Titus replied.

"My narrow escapes from the frenzied rage of several mobs I can understand," Paul continued. "Men do things in the heat of passion that they would not think of in calmer moments. But to plan assassination on that boat filled with pilgrims to the Passover at Jerusalem—that is deliberate, cold-blooded murder. I did not know their bitterness went so deep."

"It will be a surprise when they discover that you are not in the company who sailed," Titus remarked. "They saw you go aboard with the rest of the party. Even if any of them saw you disembark, they would think it was but for a minute to make some hurried farewell before leaving."

"I only hope that they do not mistake some other member of the party for me," Paul replied. "That could happen in the midnight darkness on the ship."

Titus allayed his fears. "That is hardly possible," he said. "Our party will keep constant watch. Some will have to stay awake to guard the money. Since they know of the plot, they will be doubly on their guard."

"It is hard to be hated by one's own people," Paul confessed.

"Yes," said Titus. "But when you know of it, why risk their hatred unnecessarily? My advice is that you give up your idea of going to Jerusalem. Let the others take the gift. Whatever good it may do to overcome the breach in the church between Jew and Gentile will be accomplished anyway, and you will avoid any personal danger. You have been planning to go to Rome for a long time now. Why not go there and let the others deliver the offering?"

"Out of the question!" Paul retorted sharply. "The whole controversy has been so closely associated with me personally that I must deliver the gifts myself. Even if I should die, I will hold out my hands to them in death with a gift. That may be the means of healing the breach."

On and on the travelers walked. It was a weary journey of nearly three weeks through Macedonia. The delay meant that they could not get to Jerusalem in time for the Feast of the Passover, as Paul had originally hoped. The prospect of revisiting his friends in Berea, Thessalonica, and Philippi, however, made up for this disappointment. If no further hindrance arose, they would be able to reach Jerusalem for the Feast of Pentecost, seven weeks later than the Passover.

Friends greeted them in every city. At Philippi, Luke joined the party. The three of them embarked from Neapolis, the port of Philippi, and after five days of sailing reached Troas, where they joined the others from whom they had parted at

Corinth. These had broken their trip at Ephesus and had come to Troas to rejoin Paul. The money was safe, and no one had been harmed.

They had to wait at Troas a week for passage on a little coastal ship. The last night of their stay was Sunday. They met with the Christians there in a low-ceilinged room just under the roof tile on the third floor of a tenement dwelling, where Paul preached and they observed the Lord's Supper. Conscious that he might never see these friends again, Paul spoke to them until midnight. A young man named Eutychus fell asleep on the window ledge during the long service and tumbled to the street below. Rushing down the stairway, they found him lying in a lifeless heap. Paul fell down over him and threw his arms about him, then turned to the crowd and said:

"Keep calm. He is still alive."

The lad was left in the care of some women, while the others returned to the upper room to finish the service. When the service was ended, Paul sent his traveling party to the ship, which was leaving before daylight to take advantage of the prevailing winds. On the coast of Asia Minor the breeze blows only during the first part of the day, but dies down by evening. The ship would have to round an end of land to put in at its first stop at Assos. Paul could make the shorter twenty-mile journey to Assos on foot in time to catch the ship there. Meanwhile, he would get a more certain report on the recovery of Eutychus.

He stayed, therefore, until morning, keeping only Titus with him, while Luke, Sopater from Berea, Aristarchus and Secundus from Thessalonica, Gaius of Derbe, Timothy from Lystra, and Tychicus and Trophimus from Ephesus—all sent along to carry the offering safely to Jerusalem and to represent their churches—set sail.

Paul and Titus, after learning that Eutychus was out of danger, walked to Assos and went aboard. A day's sailing brought them to Mitylene on the island of Lesbos. Another day put them on the coast of Asia Minor opposite the island of Chios, just five miles distant. The next day they rounded the western end of the island of Samos and landed at the port on its southern side. Another day and they reached Miletus, on the coast of Asia, south of Ephesus.

There was cargo to unload at Miletus, which would take two days. Paul had determined not to break his trip for a visit to Ephesus, for he was anxious to get to Jerusalem by Pentecost. Consequently, he sent a messenger to Ephesus requesting the elders of the church to come to Miletus to see him. It took a good part of the first day for the messenger to get to Ephesus. Then, leaving early the next morning, the larger, more slowly moving group of elders, took all of the second day to travel to Miletus. It was nightfall when they arrived; and, as at Troas, most of the night was spent in conversing and praying together.

As preparations began to be made for the ship to push off again, Paul spoke with feeling to these brothers in Christ. He felt that he would never see them again, and to say good-by this time was like the long farewell to a loved one in death. He struggled to control himself; but, although his voice did not break, the pent-up emotion inside was overpowering.

"You yourselves know how I lived among you all the time from the first day that I set foot in Asia," he began, "serving the Lord with all humility and with tears and with trials which befell me through the plots of the Jews; how I did not shrink from declaring to you anything that was profitable, and teaching you in public and from house to house. And now I am going to Jerusalem, bound in the Spirit, not knowing what shall befall me there; except that the Holy Spirit testifies to me in every city that imprisonment and afflictions await me. But I do not account my life of any value nor as precious to myself, if only I may accomplish my course and the ministry which I received from the Lord Jesus, to testify to the gospel of the grace of God. And now I know that all you among whom I have gone about preaching the Kingdom will see my face no more. Take heed to yourselves and to all the flock, in which the Holy Spirit has made you guardians. Be alert, remembering that for three years I did not cease night or day to admonish everyone with tears. And now I commend you to God and to the word of his grace."

As he ended his address, he knelt down on the sand, with the elders all kneeling around him, and prayed. When he had finished, they all broke out in weeping, one after another throwing his arms around Paul and kissing him, sorrowing greatly because they would see his face no more. Paul had literally to tear himself away from their arms to board the ship.

Paul and his company sailed first to the island of Cos, the next day to the island of Rhodes, and on the third day they put in at Patara, on the southern mainland of Asia Minor. There they transferred from the small coastal vessel in which they had come from Troas to a large cargo ship which could risk the open sea directly to Syria. On the third day after leaving Patara, they sighted the island of Cyprus on their left, sailed on past it for another three days, and by the end of the week, landed at the great commercial port of Tyre.

The large ship in which they had been sailing unloaded most of its cargo at Tyre, which took about a week. During this time Paul and his company visited with the Christian brothers at Tyre. They tried to dissuade Paul from going to Jerusalem, for conditions there were growing more and more tense. Any unfortunate incident during his stay might mean his death. Jewish hatred of the Romans was increasing. The extremists among them were growing more intolerant and more zealous against any violation of their law. Paul, however, was not to be dissuaded, and felt his mission to Jerusalem more important than trying to save his life. The Christians from Tyre accompanied Paul to the shore, and a scene similar to that at Miletus was re-enacted. The ship took a short run to Ptolemais, where Paul and his companions spent the day with the Christians who lived there. The next morning they sailed on to Caesarea, where they disembarked.

At Caesarea they spent several days in the home of Philip. Paul had a special feeling toward Philip, inasmuch as he was one of the group of seven deacons originally appointed in Jerusalem, just as Stephen had been. Stephen, Paul had helped to kill. Any love he could show to his co-worker Philip seemed like an opportunity to repay Stephen in small measure. Philip shared Paul's views concerning Christian freedom from the law. They talked together at great length about what might happen when Paul got to Jerusalem.

"Send your gift from here, Paul, but do not go to Jerusalem yourself," advised Philip. "The gift will have its effect without you. And your life will be of vastly more worth in taking the gospel on to Rome and Spain than it would be as a needless sacrifice at the hands of unreasonable fanatics in Jerusalem."

"I must face the issue in Jerusalem," Paul insisted. "My enemies must be given no room to call me coward, nor to misrepresent me further."

While they were debating the issue, an old friend arrived. It was Agabus, the prophet from Jerusalem who had visited Antioch years before and announced the coming famine which led Paul and Barnabas to take their first offering for Jerusalem. But this time, Agabus, rather than encouraging Paul to go to Jerusalem, warned him against it.

"Jerusalem is tense, Paul," Agabus warned. "Uprisings against the Romans have been put down ruthlessly. This has only increased Jewish hatred for Rome. Outlaws with daggers under their garments are regularly assassinating their own fellow countrymen who they think do not take a strong enough stand against Rome. And you—your life would be in real danger should you return. It is reported everywhere that you deny the law. This very gift you bring will be considered treason, for it is brought to your Christian friends rather than to the Temple. Members of your party here include uncircumcised

Gentiles. Even the Christians in Jerusalem will not like that."

With these and many other warnings Agabus described the deathtrap into which Paul would be walking if he went on to Jerusalem. The others reinforced what Agabus had to say. Luke and Titus especially pressed home the fact that the Jews from Corinth who had planned to assassinate him on the ship would have revealed their thwarted plans to friends in Jerusalem. They would be on the lookout for him there. He could not remain incognito, for dozens of Jews from Asia, Macedonia, and Greece who had come to the Feast would recognize him.

But Paul was adamant. He had taken up this offering in all good faith. He was more concerned about healing the division in the Church than with saving his life from the Jews. So he would not yield an inch on his decision to go on to Jerusalem.

Finally Agabus, in the dramatic fashion of the old Jewish prophets, walked over to Paul, loosened and unwound the long girdle around Paul's waist, twisted it tightly about his own feet and wrists, and said,

"Thus says the Holy Spirit, 'So shall the Jews at Jerusalem bind the man who owns this girdle and deliver him into the hands of the Gentiles.'"

At this the whole group, some with tears, begged and pleaded with Paul to give up his trip. Paul appreciated their concern for his welfare, but was obviously a little annoyed at their unwillingness to leave the decision to him.

"What are you doing, weeping and breaking my heart?" he said sternly. "I am ready not only to be imprisoned but even to die at Jerusalem for the name of the Lord Jesus."

The others could do nothing but acquiesce in his decision and hope for the best, saying, "The will of the Lord be done."

Early the next morning the group packed up and started for Jerusalem. Both as a courtesy and for protection, several of the Christians from Caesarea accompanied them on the journey. Paul's friends were solemn, and did not talk much as they traveled, for they felt as though they were accompanying a loved one on a death walk. Unable to dissuade Paul from a course of action that appeared to them disastrous, they were left to the dumb loyalty of men who loved but could not help. Paul himself was lost in solemn thought. He had had too many warnings, both from others and from the premonitions of his own heart, not to know that this was a fateful hour for him.

"O Jerusalem, Jerusalem, that killeth the prophets, and stoneth them that are sent unto her!" . . . This cry of Jesus, first recounted to Paul by Peter, kept ringing through his ears. Jerusalem had always been hard on the prophets. Paul knew. Had he not led a mob out of the gates of that city to stone Stephen! As the shadow of the Jaffa gate broke the heat of the sun over him for a moment, the fate of Stephen came up out of his memory once more as though it had been yesterday, and he could not escape the question, "Shall I take part again in such a scene, but this time as victim?" Such a fate, however, could not deter him. He was determined, whether by life or by death, to do his utmost to heal any breach that existed between the Gentile churches and the church of Jerusalem.

Upon entering the city, the friends from Caesarea took Paul to the home of Mnason, a native of Cyprus, who had been an influential Christian in Jerusalem from the beginning. He was cordial to Paul's views, and offered him both hospitality and protection. News of their arrival soon reached James, who immediately came to see Paul at Mnason's home. A meeting with all the elders of the church was arranged for the next day, so that Paul and his friends could present their offering and report on the progress of Christianity among the Gentile churches.

They met in the large home of Mary, the mother of John Mark, which was still the main center where the leaders of the Jerusalem church gathered. Paul came to the meeting tense with excitement. This was the hour for which he had lived for months—the hour when he could lay before the Jerusalem church the tribute of the generosity of their brothers in the Gentile churches! It was not mere money he was bringing—it was faith, and love, and sacrifice, and prayer, all transformed into a visible symbol of unity in Christ. How would it be received? Would the hidden oneness of spirit that it represented be manifest at that meeting, or would his efforts fail? Paul had arisen long before daylight that morning, to lay his hopes for that meeting before Christ, and to do his best to bring the unseen forces released by prayer to bear on that significant moment.

As the meeting opened, James extended words of greeting to Paul and his friends, to which Paul was permitted to respond. "Brothers," he began, "it is the mercy of God that brings us together on this day. Both you and I have known many perils since last we met, but out of them all the Lord has delivered us. I am persuaded that his kindly providence has brought us to this hour for the high purpose of cementing our oneness in Christ, the one Lord whom we all revere and serve. To his name be glory forever and forever."

Then he came nearer to the heart of his message. "You will remember, my brothers," he continued, "how at the Council of Jerusalem you gave to me the right hand of fellowship to go to preach the gospel to the Gentiles. It was your decision, too, not to lay the heavy burden of the Jewish law on Gentile Christians. God has honored that decision in the growth of the Church in all parts of the world. Today in every land there are men who believe in Jesus, and bear heroic witness to his name.

"Wherever I have gone, I have given testimony to the faith of the church here in Jerusalem, so that your faith and love are known in all the churches. Knowing of the great needs that are yours through the manifold trials you have endured, your brethren throughout the world have desired to show their love by ministering to your necessity out of that which God has given them. It is money that I bring, but it is more than money. It is hands of love stretched out to you across the miles that separate you from your Gentile brothers. It is heartbeats and tears and prayers that I lay before you now."

There are times when strong men weep—and this was one of them. As Paul went on, there was scarcely a dry eye among his listeners. He saw that his longings and labors and prayers had not been in vain. The Spirit of Christ was fusing their hearts into a unity that long-standing custom and sacred tradition and human willfulness could not withstand. The gift from the Gentile churches was received with great gratitude, voiced in united prayer, led by James.

In the interests of making this unity permanent, the elders proposed to Paul a measure that they thought would nullify the misrepresentations made about him by his enemies.

"Brother," said a spokesman, "you see how many thousands of Jerusalem Jews there are who have become Christians, all of them zealous upholders of the law. Now, they have heard that you teach all Jews who live among Gentiles to forsake Moses, telling them not to circumcise their children, nor to follow the old customs. They will surely hear that you have arrived, and great trouble may break out over you. We have a suggestion to make to you. We have four men here who have taken a vow of purification; associate yourself with them, purify yourself with them, pay the expenses of their sacrificial offering; and then everybody will understand there is nothing in what they have been told about you."

For the sake of going as far as he could to avoid hurting the feelings of the Jerusalem Christians, and because the ceremony of purification would do him no harm, Paul consented to this proposal. To the Jew he would become a Jew in the hope of reconciling his estranged friends. The offering had done its work. If by a harmless ceremony he could deepen the effects of the work, he had no hesitation in doing it. Not long after, therefore, he entered the Temple, associated himself with these men, and arranged with the priests to pay for them all the cost of the sacrifices which would be offered at the end of a seven-day period of purification.

Near the end of the seven days, some Jews from Ephesus who had come to the Feast saw Paul in the Jewish court of the Temple with his four friends. Some time before they had seen him on the street in company with Trophimus, a well-known Greek from Ephesus, who had not been circumcised. Either by mistake or with deliberation they accused Paul falsely of having defiled the Temple by taking a Gentile into the inner Jewish court, which Gentiles could not lawfully enter.

Beginning with violent denunciations of Paul, they finally laid hands on him and stirred up the multitude in the Temple.

"Men of Israel, help!" they shouted. "This is the man who is teaching men everywhere against the people and the law and this place! Moreover, he also brought Greeks into the Temple, and he has defiled this holy place!"

An ardent campaign of instruction against the teaching of Paul had been carried on previously, so that immediately most of the crowd—though they had never seen Paul—recognized who he was. Soon surging feet and screaming voices filled the Temple with confusion.

"Away with him! Kill him!"

"Cursed be his life! He is a traitor!"

The uproar became thunderous. Garments were swung wildly through the air; handfuls of dust were scooped up from the dry ground and hurled toward the center of the mob. Scowling men, with death in their hearts, ran out into the Temple court to search the gutters for stones.

"Dog! Devil! He is not fit to live!" called a raucous voice above the crowd. "He must be stoned for blasphemy!"

Caught in a whirlpool of raging arms and fists, Paul, battered and staggering, began to sink slowly to the ground. The mob dragged him out of the Temple, and the doorkeepers shut its doors so that it would not be profaned by the riot.

A Roman Temple guard, called to the scene by the sounds of riot, tried to reach the center of the mob. But what was one soldier against so many? Turning from the fury that he could not stem, he ran for the fortress of Antonia, which adjoined the court and reported breathlessly to the commander.

"Reinforcements!" he gasped. "Quick!"

The commander was on his feet. "What is this tumult?"

The soldier, who had not seen the fallen victim, cried: "The Jews are rioting again! If we do not act quickly, it may take all our force to quell them. They seem to be in a greater frenzy than at any time since Pilate had to mingle the blood of those fanatical Galilaeans with the blood of their sacrifices! Hurry!"

The fortress, which housed the soldiers charged with keeping the peace in Jerusalem, was connected with the Temple court by two long flights of stairs. The alarm was sounded. In a moment the commander and his officers were rushing down one stairway and soldiers with drawn swords were pouring down the other.

At sight of the soldiers the mob began to fall back sullenly. In the center there was an abrupt end to fury, and what had been a vortex of violence melted away in the general withdrawal. Only then, as the center separated and cleared, did the Romans see the bleeding form of Paul lying on the ground.

"Bind him with two chains," the commander ordered, "for he must indeed be a desperate fellow."

Paul, hardly able to stand, was hauled to his feet and bound to two soldiers.

"Who is he?" demanded the commander. "With what crime is he charged?"

As though the questions were a signal, the fury of the mob was released once more. Accusations were shouted, but were lost in the confusion and clamor.

"Enough of this!" the commander cried to the crowd. Then, turning to his soldiers, he ordered, "Take him into the fortress, where he may be questioned."

Tottering and stumbling, Paul limped off between the soldiers to whom he was chained. Enraged at the loss of their victim, the mob surged forward again like howling wolves after their prey. By the time Paul reached the steps, the violence of the crowd was so great that the soldiers had to surround him and lift him on their shoulders for protection.

Just as he was about to be carried into the barracks, Paul turned to the commander. "May I have a word with you?" he asked. He spoke in Greek.

"You know Greek!" the commander exclaimed. "Then you are not the Egyptian who organized four thousand assassins to stir up revolt against Rome?"

"I am a Jew," answered Paul, "a native of Tarsus in Cilicia, the citizen of a very famous city."

The commander knew both relief and disappointment—relief because Paul was not so desperate as he had feared and the situation was not likely to get out of hand, and disappointment because he did not have in his clutches the outlaw who had secretly armed skilled guerrillas for revolt.

"I beg you, let me speak to the people," Paul pleaded.

The commander, hoping to get some light on his crime, nodded his permission.

Raising his hand for quiet, Paul faced the crowd. He was a veteran of many narrow escapes. So, although his heart was pounding from exertion, and his face was spattered with blood and grime through which drops of perspiration had made little streaks, he was perfectly in command of himself.

A hush fell on the crowd. What would this man, whom they sought to kill, say to them?

"Brothers and fathers, listen to the defense which I now make before you," Paul began.

When they heard that he spoke to them in their own dialect, the hush deepened into motionless silence.

Paul went on. "I am a Jew, born at Tarsus in Cilicia, but brought up in this city at the feet of Gamaliel, educated according to the strict manner of the law of our fathers, being zealous for God as you all are this day. I persecuted this Way to the death, binding and delivering to prison both men and women, as the high priest and the whole council of elders bear me witness."

Paul then rehearsed in vivid language his conversion on the road to Damascus to the faith he had hated and the events that followed. He continued:

"When I returned to Jerusalem and was praying in the Temple, I fell into a trance and saw him saying to me, 'Make haste, and get quickly out of Jerusalem, because they will not accept your testimony about me.' And I said: 'Lord, they themselves know that in every synagogue I imprisoned and beat those who believed in thee. And when the blood of Stephen thy witness was shed, I also was standing by and approving, and keeping the garments of those who killed him.' And he said to me, 'Depart; for I will send you far away to the Gentiles.' "

Up to that point, the crowd listened intently. But at mention of the word "Gentiles," an uproar began again and Paul's voice was drowned out.

"Away with such a fellow from the earth! For he ought not to live!" they yelled, throwing their clothes into the air and darkening the atmosphere with great clouds of dust.

"Take him inside," ordered the commander.

As they entered the building, he gave another command. "Examine him under the lash. We must find out what he has done to make the people so wrought up against him." The commander turned him over to a centurion, and left.

The centurion ordered the soldiers to lead Paul to the guard room. There they stripped his garments and tied him, in a stooping posture, to a low post to apply the lash.

As the soldier assigned to it picked up the lash to deliver the blows, Paul spoke to the centurion,

"Are you allowed to scourge a Roman citizen—and to scourge him without a trial?"

"Stop!" the centurion ordered the soldier. "Are you a Roman citizen?"

"Yes," Paul replied.

"Wait until I return," said the centurion to the soldier, and disappeared.

Rushing into the commander's quarters, he said: "Do you know what you are about to do? This man is a Roman citizen!"

"A citizen!" The commander jumped to his feet, aghast. To scourge a Roman citizen might mean the loss of his position and severe personal discipline.

"Surely he cannot be a Roman," he replied. "He is trying to deceive us to escape scourging."

"Examine him yourself," answered the centurion, as he shrugged his shoulders. "Death is the penalty for false claims to citizenship. He would be a fool to risk that."

The commander, followed by the centurion, then strode briskly to where Paul was tied to the whipping post.

"Tell me," he inquired, "are you a Roman citizen?"

"Yes," Paul replied firmly.

Taken aback that one whom he had suspected of being a common Jewish criminal should hold the coveted prize of Roman citizenship, the commander said,

"I bought this citizenship for a large sum."

"But I was born a citizen," replied Paul.

After this, Paul was untied from the whipping post and taken to a cell to await trial. He was sore and bleeding, and uncertain of the future. But he was exultant within. He had won the hearts of the Jerusalem Christians, who had accepted his offering and his behavior in good faith. Now this attack by the non-Christian community would bind the hearts of the Christians to him even more tightly. The Church was one! And if that unity could be deepened by such suffering as this, he rejoiced to be counted worthy to suffer for the name of Christ.

The next day, in order to try to discover what wrong Paul had done, the commander held a trial. All he knew thus far was that Paul had in some way offended the religious sensibilities of the Jews. He called the Sanhedrin to meet, therefore, hoping that by trying him before them he could get at the real root of the trouble. Paul was released from his bonds, and escorted by a soldier into the presence of the assembled Sanhedrin. The commander sat in a special seat at the side of the hall, with soldiers standing at attention beside him. Outside the hall there were fifty soldiers, weapons in hand, ready to act if any trouble arose.

Looking steadily into the faces of the members of the Sanhedrin until there was silence, Paul waited to speak.

"Brothers," he began, "I have lived before God in all good conscience up to this day."

Before he could say another word, Ananias the high priest called to those standing by Paul:

"Slap him on the mouth! We cannot listen to such lies here!"

A slap resounded throughout the hall. Paul's eyes blazed. Fastening his gaze on the high priest, he said heatedly:

"God shall strike you, you whitewashed wall! Are you sitting to judge me according to the law, and yet contrary to the law you order me to be struck?"

Some who stood by said to Paul,

"Would you revile God's high priest?"

"I did not know, brothers, that he was high priest," Paul replied sarcastically. "One could not tell it by his actions!"

A general murmuring was set up in the Sanhedrin, which Paul quickly observed. There was a deep hatred between the Sadducees and the Pharisees, because of marked differences, both religious and political. This unlawful act of the high priest, indulged in without consultation with the group and before testimony had been given, offended some of the Pharisees in the Sanhedrin, who were quick to show open resentment. In this Paul saw his chance to get out of a bad situation. He could not expect justice in such a court. He could only protect himself by dividing the court. If all the Pharisees refused to vote against him, he could not be condemned. So he hurled a bombshell into the confusion by crying out:

"Brothers, I am a Pharisee, a son of Pharisees! For the hope of the resurrection from the dead I am on trial!"

The resurrection from the dead was one of the most hotly disputed points between the Pharisees and the Sadducees. The Pharisees believed it; the Sadducees did not. Furthermore, the Pharisees believed in angels, to which the Sadducees were opposed. Consequently, one of the Pharisaic party stood up beside Paul, and shouted:

"We find nothing wrong in this man. What if a spirit or an angel spoke to him?"

This touched off a general uprising in the Sanhedrin. The Sadducees, in their fury, sought to lay hold of Paul. The Pharisees surrounded him to protect him. As in the mob the day before, Paul was caught in the center of a human tornado. The commander, fearing lest Paul would be torn to pieces in the melee, ordered his soldiers to march in and take Paul from them and escort him back to the barracks. This they did, and once more Paul was saved from death.

That night in his cell he had difficulty sleeping. His body was bruised and aching from two bouts with mobs. The blind hatred of the Jews was evident in the experiences of the day, and he did not know what turn events would take now. Would Roman justice protect him, or would he be sacrificed through the insistence of his enemies? As he pondered this question late into the night in prayer, he was suddenly caught up in a sense that Christ was with him and speaking:

"Take courage! As you have testified about me at Jerusalem, so you must bear witness also at Rome."

With this assurance Paul dropped off to sleep.

He was awakened early the next morning by a gentle shaking. He opened his eyes to see his sister's son, Joseph, a lad of fourteen years.

"What brings you here, Joseph?" Paul asked in surprise. "I had no idea you were within five hundred miles of Jerusalem."

"We have come to the Feast, Uncle."

"But how did you happen to hunt me out here at this time of morning?" Paul inquired.

Joseph looked about hurriedly, to make sure no ears were listening. Then in a whisper, he replied,

"There is a plot to murder you, Uncle, and I have come to tell you."

"But how do you know it?" Paul questioned.

"We heard it by accident," the lad continued. "At the inn where we are staying some men came to visit guests from Corinth. They stayed late into the night. My father did not sleep, and overheard their conversation. The men from Corinth said they had planned to kill you on the ship coming here, but you had escaped them. The others said that they would kill you here in Jerusalem."

"But how can they get me here in the barracks?" Paul asked.

"Their plans are well laid, Uncle," replied Joseph. "They are plotting with the high priest. He is to request the commander to bring you before the Sanhedrin for further questioning. On the way from the barracks to the hall of meeting, they intend to create a surprise mob scene. In the confusion, one of the men will drive a dagger into your back and escape in the crowd. There are forty of these dagger men so pledged, Uncle. They have bound themselves under a curse that they will taste no food until they have killed you. Oh, isn't there something that we can do to stop it?" the boy pleaded.

"Why did not your father come to tell me?" Paul asked.

"My father and mother have both hated you, Uncle, because you have abandoned our faith. But when they heard you had been mobbed, and when this plot came to light, their hearts softened. They could not let it happen without warning you. They sent me to tell you, thinking that my coming would arouse less suspicion than if either of them came."

"Go down to the second room on the right, Joseph, and tell the officer there that I would like to see him," said Paul.

"Sir," Paul addressed the officer when he arrived, "take this young man to the commander. He has some important news for him."

Down the corridor they went toward the commander's quarters. Standing at attention at the door until he was recognized, the officer finally spoke,

"Paul the prisoner called me and asked me to bring this young man to you, as he has something to say to you."

The commander stepped over to Joseph, took him by the hand, and led him off to another room. "What is it that you have to tell me, my boy?" he asked.

Joseph told his story. The commander listened intently. He sat in silence for a time when Joseph had finished.

"I thank you for coming," he said. "Tell no one that you have informed me of this." He then dismissed Joseph.

As soon as the lad had gone, the commander summoned two officers.

"Get ready by nine o'clock tonight a detail of troops to escort a prisoner in safety to Caesarea—two hundred infantrymen, seventy horsemen, and two hundred spearmen. Furnish a horse for the prisoner and show him every courtesy. He is a Roman citizen. Keep all plans secret. Be alert for ambush, and guard the prisoner with your life."

When the officers had been dismissed, the commander wrote a letter to the Roman governor at Caesarea.

"Claudius Lysias, to His Excellency the governor Felix, greeting. This man was seized by the Jews, and was about to be killed by them, when I came upon them with the soldiers and rescued him, having learned that he was a Roman citizen. And desiring to know the charge on which they accused him, I brought him down to their council. I found that he was accused about questions of their law, but charged with nothing deserving death or imprisonment. And when it was disclosed to me that there would be a plot against the man, I sent him to you at once, ordering his accusers to state before you what they have against him. Farewell."

At nine o'clock that night, surrounded by four hundred and seventy troops, Paul rode off into the darkness. Thirty-five horsemen led the procession, with Paul at the center; then the four hundred footmen followed, with thirty-five horsemen bringing up the rear. By hard marching, they reached Antipatris, twenty-seven miles away, the next morning. There the four hundred footmen turned back to Jerusalem, while the seventy cavalrymen went on with Paul the last twenty-seven miles to Caesarea. Arriving at the governor's palace, the officer in command turned Paul over to Felix.

Felix read the letter from Claudius Lysias.

"To what province do you belong?" he asked Paul.

"I am of Cilicia," Paul replied, "of the city of Tarsus."

Cilicia was attached to the province of Syria, over which Felix was governor. This gave him full jurisdiction over Paul's case.

"I will hear you when your accusers arrive," Felix answered.

"Keep the prisoner in Herod's palace," he ordered an officer who stood by him. "He is a Roman citizen. Give him every care."

Paul's fate was now no longer in the hands of the Jews. It was rather in the hands of the Roman governor. Paul had every confidence that the governor would sustain his innocence of any crime. For the first time in years he had nothing to do but rest.

CHAPTER 13

Living Sacrifice

FIVE DAYS after Paul's arrival in Caesarea, he was summoned to the audience room of the palace of Felix. Escorted into the spacious hall by a soldier, the prisoner saw Felix seated in a large chair on a raised platform at one end of the room. Behind Felix several soldiers stood at attention, and not far away a group of court advisers sat behind a long railing. On one side of the hall Paul's accusers were lined up—Ananias, the high priest; several leading members of the Sanhedrin; and a Roman lawyer named Tertullus, whom they had brought along to help to persuade Felix against Paul. Paul was led to the front of the hall on the side opposite his accusers, and left

225

standing. The soldier who had brought him in retired a few paces behind him.

At a nod from Felix, Tertullus arose, stepped forward toward the governor in order to make his appeal as personal as possible, and began his accusation with flattery of the governor.

"Your Excellency," he said, "since through you we enjoy much peace, and since by your provision reforms are introduced on behalf of this nation, in every way and everywhere we accept this with all gratitude."

The only true thing about this statement was the fact that they had peace at the moment—a peace imposed by ironhanded rule in suppressing revolt. The state of the nation, however, rather than improving, was constantly worsening under Felix' administration.

Tertullus continued, "I do not wish to weary you, for time is precious to one so busy as you are, but I beg you in your kindness to give us a brief hearing."

He came quickly to the point. "The fact is," he said, "we have found this man is a dangerous troublemaker, worthy of death, whose crimes Your Excellency cannot afford to look on lightly."

He then hurled three charges against Paul, which he elaborated with eloquent oratory. Paul was a stirrer up of sedition among the Jews; he was a ringleader of the sect called Nazarenes; he had tried to desecrate the Temple. The real reason for the Jews' hatred was the middle one, Paul's connection with the Nazarene sect. This, however, was no crime against the Roman government. Tertullus therefore cleverly sandwiched it in between the two other charges, which were very serious if proved. To stir up sedition among the Jews was a threat to the Empire. To desecrate the Temple was to affront a religion that enjoyed the protection of the emperor, for Judaism had won special concessions from Rome. Tertullus ended his address in a confident vein with these words:

"By examining him yourself you will be able to learn from

him about everything of which we accuse him."

When he had finished, the high priest seconded his accusations, and other members of the delegation affirmed the truth of them.

When they rested their case, Felix nodded to Paul that he could speak in his own defense.

"Your Excellency, realizing that for many years you have been judge over this nation," Paul began, "I cheerfully make my defense before you. You will readily recognize as I speak that my accusers can furnish no proof of the charges they make against me. As for stirring up sedition, it is now but twelve days since I went up to Jerusalem to worship at the Feast, a custom with which you are familiar, excellent sir. You yourself know that five of those days have been spent here, and another on the way. I was, therefore, but six days in Jerusalem, and during all that time was in the Temple carrying out a vow. I was never found arguing with anyone in the Temple or causing a riot in either the synagogue or the city. How, then, could I have stirred up sedition?

"As for being a member of what they call a 'sect,' I gladly admit that. But that is no departure from the Jewish religion; it is rather the fulfillment of it. I worship our fathers' God. I believe all that is written in the Law and in the Prophets. I cherish the same hope in God as they do, namely, that there is a resurrection of the just and the unjust. Hence, I have a clear conscience before God and man.

"The absurdity of my desecrating the Temple will be apparent to you, most excellent Felix, when I tell you that my purpose in coming to Jerusalem after a lapse of several years was to bring a gift for my own people and to offer sacrifices. I was going about this in the Temple when some Jews from Asia began a riot, with which I had nothing to do. They seized me and dragged me out to be killed. This violation of law was halted by the intervention of Lysias, the commander of the Temple garrison, who restored order and found no fault in me. Those fomenters of riot should have been here to charge me. But since they are not, let these men yonder state one fault for which I was accused when I appeared before the Sanhedrin. The only statement I made there was an affirmation of my belief in the resurrection of the dead. Is it a crime, O Felix, to affirm belief in the faith of my fathers?"

When Paul had finished, it was apparent to Felix that his accusers had no case against him. His sincerity was as obvious as their lack of sincerity; his defense as solid as their accusations were shaky. But being unwilling to risk the results of a Jewish uprising, which might follow an outright acquittal, Felix put them off with the excuse that he would reserve a final decision until he had more evidence.

Dismissing Paul, Felix said to the delegation from Jerusalem, "When Lysias the tribune comes down, I will decide your case."

With that, he bade them go. Felix then ordered the officer in charge of Paul to keep him in custody, but to allow him as much freedom as possible and to permit any of his friends to see him at any time and to render him any service they desired.

Shortly thereafter, Felix, returning from a trip with Drusilla his wife, sent for Paul. Drusilla was a beautiful young Jewess, just nineteen years of age, whom Felix had persuaded to divorce her husband and marry him. Drusilla had heard much of her famous fellow countryman, Paul, and was anxious to see him. She wanted to hear him speak on the relation of Christianity to Judaism. Then, too, Felix hoped that Paul would offer him a bribe for his freedom. Paul seemed to have sufficient funds to take care of himself during his imprisonment, and Felix supposed also that he had control over other people's funds because of his statement in his defense that he had brought a large gift to Jerusalem. Always on the lookout for opportunities to enrich himself, Felix supposed that Paul might be willing to exchange a handsome sum for the gift of freedom.

Instead of offering him a bribe, however, Paul spoke earnestly to him about moral living, about self-mastery, about the future judgment of God on men's lives. He spoke with such point and such conviction that Felix' conscience began to prick him. He began to see something of the darkness of his own heart in the light of God's holiness, and he was afraid.

"You may go for now," he interrupted Paul. "When I can find time, I will send for you again."

This Felix did several times. He was fascinated by Paul, yet he feared his message. But as time went on, his fear of Paul's message grew less, for he did not obey it; and his desire for a bribe increased. Paul, however, offered him no bribe. For two years, Felix kept Paul a prisoner, free to do as he pleased within his own quarters. At the end of this period, because of increasing trouble with the Jews, Felix was recalled by Nero to Rome. In the hope of ingratiating himself with the Jews, he left Paul a prisoner. This did him little good, however, with the Jews; for they carried complaints against him to Rome, and only through the intercession of Felix' brother with Nero was his life spared.

Porcius Festus succeeded Felix as governor of Judea. He inherited a difficult job. The sicarii, or dagger men, among the Jews were numerous and fanatical. They had killed a high priest, Roman soldiers, Greek merchants, fellow Jews. Desperadoes in the cities and guerrilla bands in the country had inaugurated a reign of terror which was rapidly drifting toward civil war. In order to try to appease Jewish hatred, Festus made a trip to Jerusalem three days after he arrived on the job at Caesarea. No sooner had he reached Jerusalem than the high priest and the Jewish leaders demanded that he summon Paul to Jerusalem for trial. Their plan was to ambush the party en route and to murder Paul before he reached the Holy City.

Festus refused their request, but told them that they should send competent men with him to Caesarea when he returned, who could lay before him there the charges against Paul. After

eight or ten days Festus returned to Caesarea, taking with him
the Jewish representatives who were to plead the case against
Paul. They made many charges, none of which they could sub-
stantiate. Paul defended himself, as before, by insisting that
he had wronged neither the Jews nor the Temple nor Caesar.
But Festus, seeing the passion with which the Jews hated Paul,
decided that it would be to his interest to concede all he could
to them. Turning to Paul, he asked,

"Do you wish to go up to Jerusalem, and there be tried on
these charges before me?"

Paul saw through this immediately. Going to Jerusalem
would involve the possibility of death at the hands of fanatical
assassins. By thus exposing him to this danger, Festus would
gain the favor of the Jews and yet avoid violating Roman law
with an unjust condemnation. Paul, therefore, had recourse to
his rights as a Roman citizen to escape this plot.

"I am standing before Caesar's tribunal," Paul replied. "For
two years I have been a prisoner of a Roman governor. The
Roman court is here. Why should I go to Jerusalem to be
tried? I have done no wrong whatever to the Jews—you know
that perfectly well. If I am a criminal against Rome, if I have
done anything which by Roman law deserves death, I do not
object to die; but otherwise no one can give me up to these
enemies. I am a Roman citizen. I appeal to Caesar!"

Festus was somewhat taken aback at this, for Paul had completely upset his plans to gain favor with the Jews. He con-
sulted with the council of advisers, who assured him that Paul
had enough friends to press the case before Caesar if Festus refused to grant his legitimate request. Festus had worked himself into a dilemma. If he saved himself with the Jews, he
risked himself with Caesar. If he saved himself with Caesar,
the Jews would hate him. He feared Caesar, however, more
than he feared the Jews. So, returning to the judgment seat,
he said to Paul,

"You have appealed to Caesar; to Caesar you shall go!"

At this Paul rejoiced. His chances of justice at Rome would be much better than at Jerusalem, for he had never yet been the victim of any serious violation of justice at the hands of Roman officials. Furthermore, whatever the outcome at Rome, he would in this way finally get to the imperial city, to which he had dreamed of going for years. There was some time between the decision to send him to Rome and his departure, during which Paul had many conversations with Philip and other friends in Caesarea, who came to see him each day. Aristarchus and Luke were in constant attendance upon him as servants, which Roman law allowed to prisoners who were Roman citizens. Waiting fretted Paul, as always, but he endured it in good spirits, buoyed up by the fellowship of his friends and the prospect of fulfilling his lifelong desire to see Rome.

During this period of waiting, King Agrippa II and his sister Bernice, who were Drusilla's brother and sister, paid a state visit to Festus. Agrippa had had wide experience in handling questions of Jewish custom and law. Festus, therefore, decided to lay Paul's case before him in order to know what sort of report to make to Caesar in sending Paul to Rome as a prisoner of state. He told Agrippa of the trial, of how he was at a loss as to the questions of Jewish religion about which the case centered, and of Paul's appeal to Caesar.

"I should like to hear the man myself," said Agrippa.

"Tomorrow you shall hear him," Festus replied.

The next day Paul was summoned once more to the audience hall of the governor's palace. As he was led into the room, he saw more pomp and splendor than on any of his previous visits. Bernice was one of the most glamorous women in public life in the Roman Empire, for by her beauty she had mastered kings and swayed the heart of the Roman general Titus, who later became emperor. She always saw to it that a setting was provided that would set off her charms. Agrippa too was not averse to glitter and show. There they sat—crowned, bejeweled, robed in brilliant finery, with Festus at their side dressed in the full regalia of his office. Behind them, and stretching far around the wall on either side, was a double row of helmeted soldiers, standing at attention as stiffly as statues. All the military commanders were there, seated according to their rank. Besides them, the court advisers and the prominent civilians of the city had been invited to enhance the importance of this state occasion. Agrippa and Bernice were doing their utmost to impress Festus. Festus, not to be outdone, had laid himself out to prove that a Roman governor did not take second place to a king who ruled by Roman sufferance. As for the rest, they were proud to be included in the occasion, and each acted as though all the fanfare were held in his special honor.

Into this magnificent gathering came Paul, led by a soldier. He was an object of curiosity to all, and the one to whose lot it fell to provide entertainment for the crowd. A lesser man would have been overawed by the demands of that hour, but to Paul it was an invaluable privilege. He was a veteran of great occasions and felt quite at home before this crowd. Furthermore, he represented a greater king than Caesar. He was the ambassador of the King of Kings and Lord of Lords. His spirit rose to the occasion, and he was restless to begin speaking. When Paul had taken his position before the group, Festus opened the meeting.

"King Agrippa and all who are present with us," he began, "you see this man about whom the whole Jewish people petitioned me, both at Jerusalem and here, shouting that he ought not to live any longer. But I found that he had done nothing deserving death; and as he himself appealed to the emperor, I decided to send him. But I have nothing definite to write to my lord about him. Therefore I have brought him before you, and especially before you, King Agrippa, that, after we have examined him, I may have something to write. For it seems to me unreasonable, in sending a prisoner, not to indictate the charges against him."

Paul looked toward Agrippa. Agrippa nodded to him and said, "You have permission to speak for yourself."

Stretching forth his hand in a characteristic gesture, as though inviting the careful attention of all present, Paul began his appeal:

"I think myself fortunate that it is before you, King Agrippa, I am to make my defense today against all the accusations of the Jews, because you are especially familiar with all customs and controversies of the Jews; therefore I beg you to listen to me patiently."

Paul then rehearsed his life from his youth up, showing how he, as a Pharisee, had always had a deep loyalty to the Jewish law. Thinking that it was his duty to oppose Jesus, he frantically strove to put down all his followers. His vision of the living Jesus on the road to Damascus, however, had completely turned him around. After giving a gripping description of that vision and the commission to be a witness for Christ to all men, he continued:

"Wherefore, O King Agrippa, I was not disobedient to the heavenly vision, but declared first to those at Damascus, then at Jerusalem and throughout all the country of Judea, and also to the Gentiles, that they should repent and turn to God and perform deeds worthy of their repentance. For this reason the Jews seized me in the Temple and tried to kill me. To this day I have had the help that comes from God, and so I stand here testifying both to small and great, saying nothing but what the prophets and Moses said would come to pass: that the Christ must suffer, and that, by being the first to rise from the dead, he would proclaim light both to the people and to the Gentiles."

At this, Festus, who as a Roman knew nothing of the resurrection from the dead, interrupted Paul and cried out:

"Paul, you are mad! Your great learning is turning you mad."

"I am not mad, most excellent Festus," Paul replied, "but

I am speaking the sober truth. For the king knows about these things, and to him I speak freely; for I am persuaded that none of these things has escaped his notice, for this was not done in a corner."

Then, addressing Agrippa directly, Paul said:

"King Agrippa, do you believe the prophets? I know that you believe."

Agrippa interrupted him. "In a short time," he said, "you think to make me a Christian!"

"Long or short," Paul quickly replied, "I would to God that not only you but all my hearers today could be what I am—barring these chains!"

As he said this, King Agrippa arose, and Paul knew that his defense was over. The soldier who accompanied Paul pulled him to the side of the hall. The whole audience rose to its feet as one man. Agrippa and Bernice, accompanied by Festus, slowly walked the length of the hall to the entrance, followed by the other dignitaries in order. Just as they reached the door, there was a blare of trumpets, and they disappeared from Paul's sight through an armed guard which stood at attention in the long corridor.

Agrippa and Festus met with the council of advisers in a private audience room to discuss the matter.

"This man has done nothing to deserve death or imprisonment, has he?" asked Festus.

"Nothing," replied Agrippa. "If he had not appealed to Caesar, he might have been set free."

Festus still was perplexed as to what charges to file against Paul when he sent him to the emperor. But Paul had appealed to the emperor, so to the emperor he must go. Festus held him in Caesarea until he was ready to send a party of condemned prisoners to Rome to amuse the populace by throwing them to the lions in the amphitheater.

When the day for sailing arrived, Paul was handed over to an officer of the imperial regiment, named Julius, in company with the other prisoners. They could find no direct passage from Caesarea to Rome, so they boarded a vessel of Adramyttium, which was headed for ports in Asia Minor. Sailings from Asia Minor ports to Rome would be frequent, so they planned to change ships wherever they could find one headed directly for Rome.

Julius was very friendly toward Paul. His leniency was apparent the day after they sailed. The boat put in at Sidon on that day to stay for some hours, whereupon Julius permitted Paul to leave the ship and visit his friends there. Luke and Aristarchus accompanied him, for they had embarked on the journey to Rome with Paul, continuing to act as his servants. Embarking from Sidon, they had hoped to sail across open sea to the south of Cyprus, directly to the southern coast of Asia Minor. A contrary western wind, however, was too stiff to head into, so they sailed to the east of Cyprus to get whatever protection from the wind the island could afford. Then coming in close to the southern coast of Asia Minor, they turned westward and were carried by intermittent land breezes and a westward current to Myra, a leading seaport of Lycia.

At Myra, Julius found a ship from Alexandria bound for Italy, and put the whole party aboard. This was one of the larger trading ships which carried grain from Egypt to Rome, on which a large complement of passengers could be accommodated. From the time the captain gave orders to cast off from Myra, they had difficult going. Trying to head into a prevailing wind, when their course was almost due west, was difficult indeed. They had to take advantage of brief spells of land breeze and of minor shifts in the direction of the sea breeze. The sailors worked hard constantly, tacking back and forth in a zigzag fashion, having to take care at every moment not to be driven against the rocks of the shore along which they were sailing. Progress was slow and they took a week to make the normal run of two days or less from Myra to a point just off Cnidus, the southwestern tip of Asia Minor. Here they could either put into port and wait for favorable winds to sail west or they could turn south toward Crete, then hug the southern coast of Crete as they had done that of Asia Minor. In order not to lose any time, they chose the latter course.

They made fair progress until they rounded the eastern end of the island of Crete, where again they had to head into the wind, but with the protection of the shore. With great difficulty they coasted along the shore line of southern Crete until they came to a place called Fair Havens. This was the last harbor before reaching Cape Matala, where the coast line turns sharply to the north. Now fighting the wind would be more difficult, for they would lose the protection of the shore and the help of the land breeze. It was by that time late in the fall, not long before the time when all sailing on the Mediterranean would cease for the winter; and it was not safe to venture on to Rome. The question, then, was whether to winter at Fair Havens or to try to make the forty miles farther west to Port Phoenix, a harbor better situated for spending the winter.

Julius, an army officer with rank superior to the master of the ship, had to make the decision, but he naturally conferred at length with those who knew more about sailing than he. In the consultation, Paul was asked for his advice. He knew the Mediterranean well, and knew how treacherous it could be at that time of year. He felt that it was unsafe for them to venture, and counseled spending the winter at Fair Havens, undesirable though it was.

"Sirs," he said, "I perceive that the voyage will be with injury and much loss, not only of the cargo and the ship, but also of our lives. My advice is that we do not venture forth."

"But," argued the master of the ship, "this harbor is open to nearly half the compass and affords no protection against the winter storms. If we winter here, we may be beaten to pieces at anchor. If we can make it to Phoenix, we shall be safe. It is but a forty-mile run. Let us wait for a shift in the wind. If we unfurl to a southerly breeze, we can make the run in a few hours."

"The wind shifts here with great suddenness at this time of year," Paul countered. "To move out of here with a southerly breeze might get us no farther than Cape Matala, where we should be helpless against a sudden squall."

Julius finally put aside Paul's caution and decided to risk the advice of the ship's master. After waiting a few days, one morning their chance came. A moderate southerly breeze came up at dawn. All hands were quickly pressed into service. They weighed anchor, unfurled the mainsail which lazily cupped to the breeze, and slowly slid west along the shore line. Although there was little sign of it, all hands knew that the first hour was a dangerous one. Just six miles west of Fair Havens, Cape Matala projects well out to the south. With the wind blowing from the south, they could with difficulty head sufficiently into it to round the cape safely. But if the wind shifted just one degree toward the west, it would drive them into the rocks along the coast.

As they neared the cape, they got too close in shore to be comfortable. Jagged rocks showed like dragon teeth opening and closing as the waves covered them and then fell back. Sufficient speed had to be maintained to steer, but a sudden blow from the wrong direction at that speed would have dashed them to pieces. Every man on board had a stake in the process! Every eye scanned the shore line as though there were an energy in their very gaze that might push the ship away from the rocks! Every second seemed like a minute! The ship was not more than twenty feet away from shore when she finally rounded the point and headed for open sea. The relief was so great that some on board thought they could hear the ship herself heave an audible sigh of relief, and settle down in the satisfaction of having won a battle for her life.

The early morning sun was bright and the sky cloudless. As the morning wore on, however, the heat began to get oppressive. The breeze slackened until at times the air was dead still and the sail hung in lifeless folds. Perspiration stood out on every brow. Garments stuck to their skin. It was hard even to breathe. Heat rose from the deck of the ship like the blast from an open oven. As Paul looked up to the seven-thousand-foot peaks of the Cretan mountains, he saw a heat haze beginning to gather. Soon the rays of the sun began to stream brokenly through this haze, like long fingers dipping down to gather water from the sea. Gradually the haze thickened, turned to a deep gray, then black.

"Do you see what is going on up there on the mountain?" Paul spoke to the ship's captain.

"I wish I couldn't see it," he replied. "But we haven't far to go. Less than thirty miles now. Maybe the wind-gods will play with themselves up on the mountain and not bother us with their game until we reach Phoenix."

Paul knew there were no wind-gods, but he knew there was

wind, and this was no time to correct the captain's paganism. "That can be on us in no time," Paul protested. "Storms hit without warning here. Every preparation should be made before it strikes."

By that time Julius had joined them. He had a serious look as he riveted his eyes on the threatening clouds, which by this time had blotted out the top of the mountains.

"This man is right," Julius said to the ship's master. "May the gods grant us haven in Phoenix. But if not, every precaution should be taken."

To the master of the ship this judgment was an order. Walking to the front of the high, square deck on the stern of the ship where they had been conversing, he called out in a loud voice, "All hands on deck!" Immediately the entire crew of the ship was at attention. "Ready the ship for storm!" he shouted. "Life lines up! Cover all hatches! Lash down everything that moves! Take in the boat! Then stand by to lower the sail if she hits us."

Immediately the ship was a beehive of activity. Strong life lines were strung back and forth across the deck to which men could hold in a heavy sea to avoid being washed overboard. The prisoners, most of whom were kept below deck, were brought up out of the hold and the hatches covered. Then all movable objects were being lashed to the deck, when—with indescribable suddenness—the storm struck.

Like the wail of a cosmic siren, the wind began to rush through the rigging. Darkness settled in as though some wind-god had thrown a large black blanket across the ship. It was too late to take in the lifeboat, which was being towed along behind—too late even to lower the great sail. The wind caught the big canvas with a force that almost wrenched the mast from the hull, and nearly rolled the ship completely over. They were powerless to fight the hurricane; their only hope lay in surrender to it. So they turned the ship to the course of the gale, and scudded along before it.

Every man on board gave himself to but one concern—to keep from being washed overboard. Each grabbed whatever was nearest—life lines, mast, windlass, rail, ladder, stanchion— anything to which he could cling. The boat sometimes leaped as though she would be thrown clear out of the water; then she would plunge with a mighty shudder down into the raging caldron, while the waves washed over the deck. There were several times when not a soul on board expected her to emerge again. But, refusing to stay down, she rallied and raised her head to the storm to fight it out once more.

Weird shapes whirled in the black sky, as though an inferno had dumped out a thousand wily demons to battle each other. Rain fell in torrents, which, mixed with the salt spray of the swirling billows, stung the faces of crew and passengers until it was impossible for them to keep their eyes open. Lightning began to zigzag across the sky with frightful shocks. The crashing thunder that followed only made the darkness more eerie. With each twist of the ship, the planks groaned and screeched as though they were in pain. How long could they stand this without going to pieces? How much water was seeping in through cracks and hatches? Would a sudden gust tear the sail to shreds and leave them utterly helpless? Storm was king. Terror reigned. No human action was possible. The steersmen, when the tempest caught them, had quickly lashed the two rudders in a straight position. Beyond that, there was not a single thing that anyone could do to avert tragedy. They could only cling to the boat and—wait.

After nearly two hours of this—it seemed like eternity—they were blown under the lee of the island of Clauda, where the land shielded them sufficiently to reduce the violence of the storm. The steersmen, taking quick advantage of this, unlashed the rudders and gently turned the nose of the ship slightly westward to bring her even more under the protection of the island. The captain, crawling along on hands and knees in short stages between heavy blows, finally made his way to the sailors, who were clinging to the deck near the prow of the boat.

"Undergird the ship with cables!" he shouted. "If the storm continues, she'll need it. This will be our one chance."

Only those nearest him heard what he said, but the others soon guessed what the order was. Immediately, several of the sailors tied ropes around their waists, secured them to the windlasses on the deck so that they could pull themselves back if thrown overboard, and skillfully went to work at their task. Uncoiling long strands of heavy rope cable, they fastened one end to large metal hooks near the center of the boat, carried them forward to the prow, dropped enough slack to allow them to pass beneath the ship, then carried the other end back to the center of the ship on the side opposite to where they had begun. Throwing the loose end around a capstan, they wound it as tightly as they could. This was repeated until several large cables undergirded the boat, reinforcing the strength of the hull so that the twisting of the planks would not so readily produce leaks.

This done, the next task was to haul in the boat that had been dragging along behind the ship. In smooth weather, the boat was always towed in this fashion, but in stormy weather it was hoisted up on deck and lashed down to make it secure. The storm had struck with such suddenness that the boat could not be hauled in before. By this time, it was quite full of water and was very difficult to handle in a rough sea. The sailors crawled back toward the stern, anchored themselves to the rail, with great effort hoisted it up, emptied it of water, and lashed it in place on deck.

"Haul down the sail!" was the next order. This had been impossible to do while they were in the direct path of the storm, but the temporary protection of the island enabled them, though with difficulty, to lower the great sail now. Their reason for doing it was that if it remained up, they would have to continue scudding before the wind, and would soon land

in the shallows and quicksands of the Syrtis off North Africa—
the fear of every Mediterranean sailor in those days. They
lowered not only the sail, but the long yard, with all the spars,
so that not a stick of wood remained in the air but the large
mast which could not be brought down. They then ran up, on
a little mast near the prow of the ship, a small storm sail, which
would give the ship enough motion to be steered, but would
not place her in danger of being rolled over by the gale. Turning the ship's head offshore a little to the west, they set out
across the sea once more, hoping that by skillful seamanship
they could keep clear of Africa and outride the storm.

Night came on. The storm blew on with unabated fury. No
food could be taken. No sleep was possible. The screaming of
the wind and the groaning of the twisting ship made conversation out of the question. No lamp could be lighted to break
the blinding darkness. It was a night of terror, with every man
on board occupied with the sole task of anchoring himself in
some way so as to avoid being washed into the raging sea.

Paul had started for Rome. Would he make it? He had appealed to Caesar to escape death at the hands of wicked assassins. Would he meet death by the violence of the sea? He
had written once to his friends at Corinth, "O death, where is
thy victory?" He was having an opportunity now to face the
monster in his own territory.

Morning came, but no letup of the storm. The twisting of
the ship had let in sufficient water so that the sailors had to set
to work pumping frantically. It seemed a hopeless struggle to
fight back the incoming sea. To lighten the ship, they began
to throw out some of the cargo. This raised the hull so that
less of its leaky surface was constantly under water. Furthermore, with less weight in the hold, the battered ship would
not be so likely to go to pieces under the ceaseless hammering
of the waves. For two more days the desperate men fought constantly to keep afloat. On the third day they threw overboard
all the ship's gear—the main yard, the mainsail, the rigging.

The storm raged on. They could not calculate their position, for neither sun nor stars could be seen. The leakage was gaining on their desperate efforts. Weakness was increasing from lack of food, loss of sleep, and constant toil. The instinct for self-preservation kept both crew and passengers blindly battling, but they had given up all hope of being saved.

Eleven more days and nights dragged on, when the storm began to abate somewhat. It became apparent that the ship would not go to pieces now, for she had ridden out the worst of the storm, but she was filling with water so rapidly that they felt they could never reach any shore before she foundered. At this point, Paul stood up in the midst of the disheartened crowd of nearly three hundred men, and spoke to them.

"Men," he cried, "you should have listened to me, and should not have set sail from Crete and incurred this injury and loss. I now bid you take heart; for there will be no loss of life among you, but only of the ship. For this very night there stood by me an angel of the God to whom I belong and whom I worship, and he said, 'Do not be afraid, Paul; you must stand before Caesar; and lo, God has granted you all those who sail with you.' So take heart, men, for I have faith in God that it will be exactly as I have been told. But we shall have to run on some island."

That night, the fourteenth since they had sailed, about midnight the sailors began to sense that they were nearing land. Above the noise of the heavy sea they thought they could hear the breakers dashing on the shore. They took a sounding and found the depth twenty fathoms. A little later they sounded again, and found it but fifteen fathoms. They were coming to land! But to run aground in the darkness would have meant death. Quickly, therefore, the storm sail was furled, the rudders were pulled out of the water and tied up, and four anchors were let go from the stern of the ship. Such anchoring was an unusual procedure, but it kept the boat nosed in toward shore, which would make it easier to beach the next day.

The sailors unlashed the boat from the deck, and began to lower it into the water under the pretext of letting down additional anchors from the bow of the ship. Their real intention, however, was to make for shore in the little boat, since they feared that the larger ship might be beaten to pieces at anchor during the night. The watchful eye and alert thinking of Paul sensed their intention.

Stepping up to Julius, Paul said, "Unless these men stay in the ship, you cannot be saved." He knew that all hands would be needed to beach the ship the next morning.

"Cut the ropes!" Julius ordered his soldiers. The ropes were cut and the boat fell into the abyss below. They then settled down to the long, slow process of waiting out the night.

Just before daybreak, Paul begged them all to take some food. "Today is the fourteenth day," he said, "that you have continued in suspense and without food, having taken nothing. Therefore I urge you to take some food; it will give you strength, since not a hair is to perish from the head of any of you." He then made a prayer of thanks, after which they all took some food. Their strength somewhat renewed from this, they made final preparations for beaching the ship. They pumped out water with renewed energy. The remaining cargo of wheat was dumped into the sea to lighten the boat as much as possible.

When day broke, they did not recognize the shore. It was rock-bound and dangerous, but they noticed an inlet with a sandy beach. Cutting the anchor cables, unlashing the rudders, and hoisting the little storm sail, they made for this spot. Shortly they drove the ship aground. The prow stuck fast in the mud, but the stern began to break up under the beating of the waves.

"Let us kill all the prisoners, sir," said one of the soldiers to Julius. "They will swim ashore and escape, and it will be our lives for theirs."

But Julius wanted to save Paul, for he had come to trust his judgment and felt he could not get on without him. "Touch not a single prisoner!" he ordered. Then, turning to the entire group, he said: "Let all who can swim jump overboard and make for land. Let those who cannot swim take hold of a piece of wreckage. It will keep you afloat and the waves will wash you ashore." In this way, not a life was lost, but all made it safely to land.

They discovered that they had been cast up on the shores of the island of Malta. The natives treated them kindly, building a fire to warm and dry them, and providing them food. They were greatly taken with Paul through an unusual happening. In order to show his appreciation to the natives for their kindness, Paul went to the edge of a nearby woods and gathered a large bundle of sticks for the fire. As he laid them on the burning pile, a viper crawled out of one and stung him in the hand. The natives supposed it to be poisonous, and said one to another:

"No doubt this man is a murderer. Though he has escaped from the sea, justice has not allowed him to live."

They watched him closely, expecting to see him swell up, or drop over dead. But when nothing happened to him, they changed their minds and said, "He must be a god!"

The ruler of the island, a man named Publius, had his estate near the scene of the wreck. He invited Paul, Luke, Aristarchus, Julius, and the master of the ship to stay with him for three days, and showed them great kindness. The father of Publius happened to be ill. Paul prayed for him, and he became better. As a result of this, many sick were brought to Paul for healing. During three months, Paul and Luke served the people of the island, preaching to them, healing their sick, and helping them in every way that opportunity afforded. When the seas were safe for sailing again, the islanders, loath to have them leave, gave them gifts and supplies to see them through on their journey to Rome.

They set sail once more on a ship from Alexandria which

had wintered at Malta. They touched at Syracuse in Sicily and Rhegium in southern Italy, and finally landed at Puteoli, in the Bay of Naples. Julius was anxious to see friends there after a long absence, so he spent a week before moving on to Rome. He permitted Paul freedom, and Paul, Luke, and Aristarchus found some Christian brothers with whom they spent the week. At the end of that time, they set out on foot for Rome, one hundred and forty miles away. When they reached the Appii Forum, about forty-three miles south of Rome on the Appian Way, they met some of the Christians from Rome who had heard of their approach and had come out to meet them. Ten miles farther on, at the Three Taverns, another and a larger party of Christians joined them.

Paul was deeply moved by the sight of these brothers, and he saw that the Christian Church was already firmly rooted in the capital of the world. It was a joy to get acquainted with men to whom he had before written a letter but whom he had never met. Although he was a prisoner, he was also among friends. If Christianity were thus thriving in Rome, surely he would be acquitted by Caesar, and would realize his dream of preaching the gospel in the leading city of the world.

Suddenly, there in the distance, he saw journey's end— Rome.

CHAPTER 14

𝔐ore than 𝔠onqueror

I AM NOT ASHAMED of the gospel," Paul had written to the Christians at Rome a few years before. Now, led through the gate of Rome chained to a soldier, in company with a group of condemned criminals, taunted by street loafers, derided by every passer-by, he was having opportunity to put his declaration to the test.

Paul's first night in Rome was spent in a prison cell. The next day, lining up the entire group of prisoners from Caesarea, Julius reported to the stratopedarch, the officer in charge of the barracks where the imperial couriers had their headquarters.

"All condemned but one," Julius addressed the stratopedarch, handing him a letter from Festus.

"To the court of my lord the emperor," the stratopedarch began to read, "the following prisoners have been tried according to Roman law, found guilty, and condemned to death." Their names and crimes were then listed, followed by a personal greeting and the official seal of Festus.

With every prisoner identified and accounted for, soldiers were ordered to lead them off to death cells to await their turn in the arena, either as gladiators or as victims of hungry lions.

"And what of this one?" asked the stratopedarch when all the prisoners were gone but Paul.

"An unusual case," replied Julius. "Sent without charges."

"Without charges?" replied the magistrate in surprise. "Is Festus low on prisoners, that he sends them with no accusation?"

Opening a letter as he spoke, he read: "This man might have been set free, had he not appealed to Caesar. He is accused by the Jews of violating their religious customs, but has done nothing contrary to Roman law. I am at a loss as to how to indict him, but have sent him at his request to Caesar's court, where his accusers may press their charges and get a final verdict. Farewell. FESTUS."

"What do you know of him, Julius?" inquired the magistrate as he laid the letter aside.

"An innocent man," replied Julius, "a religious teacher who has great powers. Helps everyone, harms no one. Saved us from perishing in storm at sea. I have never seen anyone like him."

"Will he try to escape?"

"Never!" affirmed Julius.

"Then let him live in his own quarters under guard until his case is called," ordered the stratopedarch. "Visitors may come and go as they like."

When Paul was led back to his cell, his request was granted that Luke be admitted to see him. "Go in search of lodging for us," said Paul. "I am to be permitted to live in my own quarters under guard until my trial. Find some place large enough to accommodate you and Aristarchus besides me and a soldier. The Christians will help you to find a place."

A second night Paul spent in his prison cell, but by noon the next day Luke had located a place for him to live. It was in a humble section of the city, but had ample space to house Paul's party, besides room for guests who might come to visit him. The first thing Paul did in his new quarters, after welcoming the many Christians who came to see him, was to invite the leading Jews of Rome to visit him. This was in accord with his lifelong custom of beginning his work in any new center with his own people. Furthermore, thinking that the Jews of Jerusalem would have sent accusations against him to the Jews at Rome, he hoped to clear himself of these charges and win the favor of the Roman Jews.

When the men of influence among the Jews assembled, Paul addressed them: "Brothers, although I have done nothing against the people or our ancestral customs, I was handed over to the Romans as a prisoner from Jerusalem. They meant to release me after examination, as I was innocent of any crime that deserved death. But the Jews objected, and so I was obliged to appeal to Caesar—not that I had any charge to bring against my own nation. This is my reason for asking to see you and have a word with you. I wanted you to know that I am innocent of any crimes of which you may have heard, and that, rather than being against my own people, I am wearing this chain because I share Israel's hope.

"This hope for me is assured because Messiah has already come, suffered, and died; but God has raised him from the dead and exalted him at his right hand. His resurrection assures our hope of the resurrection of the dead."

"We have had no letters from Judea about you," the Jews replied, "and no brother has come here with any bad report or story about you. We think it only right to let you tell your own story; but as regards this sect, we are well aware that there are objections to it on all hands."

"But do you do right to listen to the objections before you have examined the evidences of its truth?" Paul asked. "I too once opposed this Way in my ignorance. But God, who is rich in mercy, opened my eyes to the truth. Are you willing to hear my story and examine the Scriptures for yourselves?"

To this they agreed, and a time was set when it would be convenient for the Jews to return to hear Paul's message. On the appointed day they came in large numbers, crowding to capacity the space within the house and overflowing into the yard. Paul spent the entire day telling of his own opposition to Christianity in the beginning, of his sudden conversion, and of his experiences through a busy and rugged life since that time. He sought also to show them that both Moses and the prophets could be rightly understood only in the light of their fulfillment in Jesus.

A great discussion followed. "Salvation is only for those who are circumcised, and is achieved by keeping the law," some insisted.

"What do the Scriptures say?" countered Paul. "Take Abraham, for example. Was he saved by keeping the law? Is it not written, 'Abraham believed God, and it was reckoned unto him for righteousness'? When this happened, was he a circumcised man? He was not; he was still uncircumcised. It was *afterwards* that the sign of circumcision was given to him, as a seal upon that righteousness which God was accounting to him *as yet an uncircumcised man!* Abraham, therefore, was saved by faith before he was circumcised, and long before the law of Moses was given. If Abraham was saved by faith and not by the works of the law, so also are we. For both Jew and Gentile, it is a matter, not of achieving, but of believing."

"If God intended to save men by faith, why, then, was the law ever given?" came an objection.

"The law was not given to save us, but to show us how badly we need saving," came Paul's answer. "The law is the straight-edge that shows us how crooked we are. For example, I should never have felt guilty of the sin of coveting if I had not heard the law saying, 'Thou shalt not covet.' But commanding me not to covet did not save me from coveting—it merely set the stage for me to covet. So that the commandment, which was meant to be a direction to life, became a sentence to death."

"If keeping the law does not save us, but God's grace through faith, why not, then, sin all the more?" came a further question. "Wouldn't it be that the greater the sin, the more wonderful the faith, and the more glorious God's mercy in forgiving it?"

"You do not understand the wonder of God's mercy," replied Paul. "If Christ died for our sin, we too must die to it. That is the meaning of baptism. When the water flows over us, it is as though we were in the grave with him. And as he was raised, so we too share his new life. To know what sin has cost God is to abhor it and flee it. To know the power of Christ's resurrection is to know a power to triumph over sin. Sin is no longer the master of a man living under grace. Released from the service of sin, he enters the service of righteousness."

And so the discussion went on at length—many questions, many comments favorable and unfavorable, many decisions for and against the new faith. As they were about to leave, Paul reminded them of Isaiah's warning against closing their minds to the truth, and insisted that the truth would triumph whether they accepted it or not. "Be certain of this," he concluded, "the salvation of God has been sent to the Gentiles; they will listen to it, even if you will not."

Although the majority of the Jews did not accept Paul's teaching, his work in Rome was too indirectly connected with their interests to arouse their vigorous opposition. Furthermore, the Jews had previously been expelled from Rome for religious rioting. Now that they were back, they felt it wise not to stir up any active opposition to Paul. He turned his attention, therefore, to the Gentiles and to his Christian friends who came to see him from all over the Empire.

Paul's trial was delayed indefinitely. No one came to press charges against him, and Nero and his court were so engrossed in pleasure that anything but the most urgent business had to await a convenient season. For two whole years, therefore, under constant guard, Paul was free to work in his own house, and to welcome all who came to him. He kept in close touch with the churches he had founded, through reports of visiting messengers and through letters which he sent back to them.

Paul's dwelling was a beehive of activity. Luke and Aristarchus, who had accompanied him on his long journey to Rome, constantly attended him and took care of his household needs and bodily wants. Timothy arrived from Macedonia, to work with Paul in Rome and to make successive trips to the Macedonian churches. Tychicus, who had helped Paul to deliver the offering to Jerusalem, arrived from Ephesus to bring news of the churches in Asia and to take letters back to them. Epaphras, who had been converted under Paul in Ephesus and had founded the church at Colossae, came to report both the progress and the needs of the Colossian church. Even Mark turned up—Mark who had deserted Paul on his first missionary journey and whom Paul had refused to take on the second journey. Mark had grown in the faith through the years and had now become profitable to Paul in his work at Rome. In addition to these, there were many local Roman Christians who frequented Paul's quarters every day.

What a time the Roman guards had! Chained to Paul's wrist, they had to endure all this coming and going, all the enthusiastic talk about a strange religion of which they had never heard, all the careful plans that were laid for strengthening the Christian work in nearly every leading center of the Empire, all the letters that Paul wrote and dispatched. A few of them were surly and resentful, making it unpleasant for Paul and his friends. Most of the guards, however, were respectful and curious. Julius and his soldiers had circulated exciting stories of Paul's behavior in the storm at sea and of his

mighty works at Malta. His fame spread throughout the Praetorian Guard, so that frequently soldiers vied with each other
for a chance to spend a few hours chained to him. To see at
close range a man on such intimate terms with the gods was
a coveted experience! A few of the soldiers even became Christians, but secretly, lest their friendship with a prisoner should
bring them under suspicion.

One evening, just at dusk, a stranger appeared and accosted
Luke outside Paul's dwelling. "Does Paul of Tarsus dwell
here?" he inquired.

"He is a prisoner in his own house here," Luke replied.

"Are you his friend?" he questioned further.

"More than friend. A brother!" replied Luke.

Although it was a hot evening, the stranger had his shawl
thrown well over his head, so that but little of his face was exposed. His garments were worn, his person not well kept, and
he spoke Greek with a broken accent.

"I would like to speak to Paul," continued the stranger,
"but in secret."

"It is impossible to speak to Paul in secret," replied Luke.
"He is constantly chained to a Roman soldier."

"But is there not some hour of the night," entreated the
stranger, taking Luke by the arm and walking farther away
from the door, "when I might see him alone?"

"He has no more privacy at night than in the daytime,"
Luke answered. "He sleeps chained to a soldier."

The countenance of the stranger dropped. He eyed the
ground for a time thoughtfully, as though he were carrying on
some sort of secret debate with himself. Finally, he spoke:

"I had better not talk with him, then, for it might not be
safe. I wanted to speak with him about a Christian friend at
Colossae, but the message is highly secret—one that the Romans should not know about. If I must talk with him in the
presence of a Roman solider, it would be too dangerous."

"Is it important?" asked Luke.

"Very," replied the stranger, "too important to risk before a Roman guard."

Luke was silent for a moment. Then he said: "Once in a while Paul's guard is a Christian. If you would come some night when a follower of the Way is to sleep with him, you might talk freely about Christian matters."

"Can you trust these Christian guards?" inquired the stranger. "Are you sure they are not informers in disguise?"

"Absolutely sure of them," replied Luke. "They have long since given evidence of their loyalty to Christ."

"Then tell me when one of them will be here at night, and I will come."

"That is impossible," replied Luke. "We never know who is coming until he gets here. If you will come to the door each night just after dark, I shall be on the watch for you and signal you away until it is safe. There is no other way."

So, night after night, this stranger crept past Paul's dwelling under cover of darkness, and night after night he was sig-

naled on by Luke. But finally one night Luke took him by the arm and led him into the dimly lighted room where Paul and the soldier were sitting.

"Brother Paul," said Luke, "I bring you a friend who has news for you from Colossae."

Paul peered at the stranger through the dull light. The shawl was still thrown over his head and his features were hidden.

"Come closer," said Paul, stretching out his hand to the stranger. "Take a seat near me here where we can talk."

The visitor came over slowly without saying a word, and hesitatingly sat down beside the apostle.

"Do you know me?" he finally asked Paul.

"If you would throw that shawl back from your face, I might," Paul replied.

The stranger, with a quick movement, threw the head covering back over his shoulders. In an instant, Paul gasped:

"Onesimus! I can hardly believe it!"

The stranger dropped on his knees, grabbed Paul about the legs, and buried his head in his lap. Heavy sobs shook his frame, while Paul laid his hand on his head.

"Tell me all, my son," said Paul after a time, raising his head. "You need have no fear. The guard here is my son in the gospel. We are all members of one family. Tell me your story."

Onesimus told his story in a few words. He was a slave of Philemon, one of the leading members of the church at Colossae. He had stolen a large sum of money from his master and fled to Rome. There he soon spent the money and was reduced to living by hunting through garbage piles at night. He lived in constant fear of detection as a slave, which would have meant crucifixion or some other ghastly form of death. His terror had become so great that even with his headdress drawn close to obscure his features and to hide the slave holes pierced in his ears, he feared to venture forth in daylight. He had for weeks been living in a foul cellar with other runaway slaves—

penniless, hungry, desperate with fear, distracted by guilt. His last hope was that he might find Paul and get help from him. So he had come.

When he had finished, Paul said: "My son, truly it is a reliable saying, and worthy of your special belief, that 'Christ Jesus came into the world to save sinners.' You have confessed your sin to me. Now confess it to God while I pray, and accept his forgiveness." Paul prayed, while a great burden rolled off the back of Onesimus. For the first time since he had run away, he felt clean inside, and hopeful, and safe.

They talked at length into the night as to what course to follow now. Paul insisted that Onesimus should return to his master Philemon, to whom by law he belonged, and do what he could to make right his wrong against him. He would write a letter to Philemon, asking him to receive him kindly as a converted brother, and not to treat him as the Roman law permitted in the case of runaway slaves. As soon as it was convenient, Paul would send someone to accompany him to Colossae in safety. In the meantime, Onesimus was to stay with Paul. He could spend the time when a non-Christian guard was on duty in the rear of the dwelling where he would be safe.

My dear Colleague [Paul took up his pen to write to Philemon], I am writing to you from prison, where I have landed as the result of serving our common Master.

I want to enlist your sympathy on behalf of a convert I have made here in prison—a veritable son born to me while in chains. It is none other than Onesimus. Formerly, I know, he proved a disappointment to you, but now he is a great credit both to you and to me. I am sending him back to you with as much affection as if he were a bit out of my own heart.

It may be that you lost him for a short time, just in order that you might possess him forever; though not now as a slave, but as a beloved brother. You can guess how much I love him, but you ought to love him much more, both for his own sake and also because he has entered the service of a fresh Master who is also yours.

I know you look on me as a friend. Very well then, receive him as you would myself. If you feel he has wronged or cheated you, put it down to my account. I've written this with my own hand: I, Paul, hereby promise to repay you.

I need not remind you that as a matter of fact you owe me far more than this—even your own hope of salvation. Now do grant me this favor, my brother—such an act of love will cheer my heart. I write in the fullest confidence, knowing you will do even more than I ask.

And by the way, please get ready a spare room for me. I hope that in answer to your prayers I shall soon be with you again.

With my prayers that Christ's grace may be with you,

PAUL.

Not long before this, Epaphras, who had founded the church at Colossae, came to Rome to tell Paul of the great progress of the church there, and also to report on some false teachers who were causing difficulty among the Colossian Christians. Since Onesimus was to be sent back to Colossae, it would be a good time to write a letter to the Colossian church.

To the Colossians, who were troubled with some pagan superstitions about worshiping angels and revering unseen spiritual powers, in addition to Christ, Paul wrote:

Continue to order your conduct under the lordship of Christ Jesus as you accepted it from Epaphras. See that you do not fall a prey to any hollow and misleading philosophizing, spun out of mere human and childish traditions about supernatural beings and quite alien from the teaching of Christ. Christ has stripped away like a cast-off garment every demonic rule and authority and made a public exhibition of them, openly triumphing over them on the cross. Since then you have risen with Christ, aim at the things that really do belong to the higher life, that life in which Christ is already enthroned, seated at the right hand of God.

All my personal news will be brought to you by Tychi-cus, my dear brother. I am sending him to you for this very purpose, so that when you know how we have fared, you may be comforted and relieved. With him I am send-ing Onesimus, another loyal and beloved brother, who actually belongs to your part of the world. They will tell you all that has taken place.

Grace be with you,

PAUL.

Paul took advantage of the situation too to write another letter, a general letter to all the churches of the province of Asia, which could be carried to them with the letter to the Colossians, and circulated among all the churches in that vi-cinity. This letter, which later came to bear the name of the Ephesian church, did not deal with any specific local difficul-ties, but was a great doxology setting forth the wonder of the gospel as it had come to men in Jesus Christ and had found embodiment in the growing Christian Church. The battle with the Judaizers was won, so Paul now gave his thought to the wonders that God intended to do through Christ, and the glories of the Church, which was Christ's Body.

How rich is the kindness [he wrote] that He has showered upon us in disclosing to us a complete explanation of his secret purpose! His purpose was to make all history work out toward one culminating moment, when he could bring every movement in the whole universe, spiritual as well as material, to a head in Christ.

Him he made to sit on his right hand in heaven far above all potentates, authorities, powers, lordships, and every other title that can be given either in this world or in that to come.

"He hath put the universe under his feet." In so exalting Christ he has made him head of a body, the Church.

The Church, to Paul, was the glorious company of all men who believed in Christ and shared his Spirit. Slaves, freedmen, rich and poor, courtiers and commoners, cultured and ignorant, Jews and Gentiles, male and female—all these were knit into a family, a community, a living temple of God, where God himself was pleased to dwell and through which he did his work in the world. It was to this glorious company that those to whom he wrote were called. Paul then set forth the high moral code for daily living that members of such a fellowship should obey, and concluded:

In order that you, as well as the others to whom I have written, may know how I am getting on, Tychicus, my dear brother and a faithful Christian minister, will bring you all the news. That is why I am sending him to you, that he may tell you everything about us. I am sure his news will give you ground for encouragement.

May God our Father and the Lord Jesus Christ grant peace to the brethren and love with faith. Grace be to all those who love our Lord Jesus Christ with undying constancy.

With these three letters, Tychicus, a native of the province of Asia, was dispatched as an escort of Onesimus. He could vouch for him on the way, and could support Paul's request that Philemon take Onesimus back as a brother, not as a slave.

Shortly thereafter Paul's case came up for trial. He did not

appear before Nero himself, but before one of the two pre-
fects of the Praetorian Guard who represented the emperor in
judicial cases at which he did not himself preside. The trial
was held in a large basilica in the Forum. The great central
nave of the basilica was open to the sky, but the aisles which
surrounded it on every side were covered by a roof held up by
huge marble pillars. At one end of the nave, seated in an ivory
chair on an elevated platform, sat the prefect. He was surrounded by the Council of Assessors, advisers who helped him
to interpret the law, although he had full responsibility for
his decisions. At the sides, near the front of the hall, were
benches for distinguished persons attending the trial. In the
center a great crowd of the populace had gathered to witness
the affair.

Paul had little difficulty in establishing his innocence. No
accusers had come from Jerusalem in two years to press charges
against him. Festus, who had sent him to Rome, had sent no
accompanying accusations. Paul had the precedent of Gallio,
Felix, Festus, and others, to plead—all of them Roman magistrates before whom he had appeared and been declared innocent of any breach of Roman law. Through his two-year
residence in Rome, he had shown himself to be a harmless
teacher of religion, and had gained the respect of many of
the soldiers and officials, and had even won some as converts
to his faith.

As the trial proceeded, he had opportunity to speak in self-
defense several times. Each time, as he had done at his former
trials, he took occasion to speak of his religious experience
and to bear witness to his faith. His story accorded with the
reports that the state had gathered from various centers of
the Empire where Paul had worked. So, from the start, things
looked favorable for an acquittal.

While the trial was in progress, Paul wrote a letter to the
church at Philippi. The Philippian Christians had sent him
a generous gift to sustain him while he was in prison. Epaphro-

ditus, who brought the gift, had intended to stay with Paul until his trial was ended. He was taken ill, however, and nearly died. Upon recovering, he was anxious to get back home. So Paul sent him on, with a letter of thanks to his friends at Philippi and word that he hoped to see them soon himself.

I should like you to know [he wrote] that my present plight has actually worked out to the advantage of the gospel. Everyone in the Praetorian Guard and elsewhere knows that I have been put in prison because I am a Christian. The consequence is that the majority of the brethren have acquired confidence from my chains and are becoming quite fearless in preaching the word of God.

I know that the outcome of all this will be my salvation through your prayers. I know that I shall still live and shall remain with you to help forward your progress. So you need put no restraint on your jubilation in Christ Jesus on my account, for I shall be with you once again.

I am hopeful soon, if it is the Lord's will, to send Timothy to you. Then I shall be cheered by a firsthand account of you and your doings. I hope to send him as soon as I can see what my own fate is to be. But I have confidence in the Lord that he will enable me shortly to come to you myself.

In spite of this I thought it necessary to send Epaphroditus back to you at once. He has been longing to see you all and has been very worried since you heard that he was sick. He was indeed very ill, so ill that he nearly died. But God had pity on him, and not on him only, but also on me, so that I should not have to bear a fresh burden of sorrow. Give him a cordial Christian welcome. You should honor men like him: he nearly died in doing the work of Christ, and risked his life to render me the services you could not be here to perform.

I am indeed overwhelmed by the present you sent through Epaphroditus. That is a fragrant and acceptable sacrifice, which must give much pleasure to God. I am sure that God on my behalf will satisfy all your needs out of the treasure of his glory in Christ Jesus.

Give my greetings to every Christian brother. The grace of our Lord Jesus Christ be with your spirit.

PAUL.

Not long after Epaphroditus was sent off with this letter, Paul's verdict was brought in—acquitted! For the first time in nearly five years, he knew once again what it was to be a free man. Although he had originally hoped to go on to Spain after seeing Rome, his first thought after being released was to return to visit some of the churches he had helped to found. In addition to revisiting some of the scenes of his former labors, he opened up new work on Crete, where he had stopped on his voyage to Rome, which Titus was left to carry on. This done, he set out for the western border of Macedonia, Nicopolis, to begin work there. It was his hope, after wintering there, to move on to the western border of the world, Spain, thus fulfilling his Lord's command to preach the gospel to the uttermost parts of the earth.

Meanwhile, things were happening in Rome. A nine-day fire broke out, completely annihilating three out of fourteen districts of the city, and gutting seven others. Whether Nero was responsible for the fire or not, the populace soon laid the blame at his door. He had admired the spectacle while it raged. He gloated over the opportunity to rebuild the city in more magnificent style. He confiscated some of the ruined area to build himself a golden house, splendid beyond description. Furthermore, the fact that the fire, when almost under control, broke out anew in the gardens of Tigellinus, his chief councilor, added suspicion to suspicion. Hatred was mounting, revolution brewing. In fear, Nero cast about for some scapegoat on whom he could pin guilt and turn attention away from himself. He chose the Christians. Did they not believe that the world was to come to a sudden end by fire? Was it not possible, then, that they had set this fire to hasten the end of the world? It sounded plausible.

In addition to charging them with the fire, he charged them as enemies of humanity and traitors to the state through their worship of Jesus as Lord. A reign of terror ensued. Christians were covered with animal skins and worried to death by wild dogs. They were crucified. They were soaked in pitch and set on fire as torches to light the imperial gardens for the Circensian games.

During this orgy of blood Paul was rearrested. The official persecution did not spread far beyond Rome, but when news of it reached the proconsul of Macedonia, he felt that it would be a feather in his cap to return to Rome the leader of the Christian movement. So back to Rome Paul was sent once more, in chains. His treatment this time was a great contrast to that of his former imprisonment. He was plunged into the Mamertine Prison and kept in rigid confinement. The first burst of passion against the Christians had subsided somewhat, but it was still dangerous to show oneself a friend of Paul. Onesiphorus, from Ephesus, hunted him out in prison and befriended him, but this threw him under such suspicion that he was put to death. Luke stood by him and escaped martyrdom only because in the eyes of the Romans he was Paul's slave. A few friends sought to minister to his needs through Luke. But when he stood trial, no one dared to defend him or pose as his friend. One of his closest companions, Demas, forsook him and fled the city, fearing for his life.

At his first appearance in court, he was charged with conspiracy in connection with the great fire. Against this charge he defended himself successfully. The second charge, that of being a monstrous criminal, a hater of humanity, grew out of the common failure to understand Christianity on the part of the first century Romans. Without images or temple, the Christians seemed godless to the Romans. Their worship of a crucified Jew seemed monstrous. Their withdrawal from the corruptions of pagan society and their severe condemnation of immorality appeared as hatred of men. Against these charges Paul knew that his chances of acquittal were slight—he would have to follow his Lord to martyrdom. But he neither feared nor resisted this. His life they could destroy; the word of God would survive, and the Church would triumph over the world.

His spirit held firm to the end. Poised on the threshold of eternity, he thought less about himself than about his churches. As a last act, he wrote a brief letter to Timothy. He warned Timothy not to be ashamed of the gospel, and to gird himself like a soldier for whatever he had to endure. Winter was setting in, and he needed a coat, which he asked Timothy to bring with all speed. If he came soon, he might see his face once more. If not—well, the ties that bind Christian to Christian do not break at death.

Christ has annihilated death and poured a flood of new light on life and immortality by means of the gospel [he wrote]. Of that gospel I have been appointed a preacher and an apostle and a teacher. That is the reason why I endure these misfortunes. But I am not ashamed of it, for I know in whom I have believed and I am certain that he is able to keep what I have deposited with him against the Last Day.

I am already offering the libation of my own life, and the moment for my departure is already here. I have played my part in the great contest; I have run my race; I have preserved my loyalty to the faith. Now I wait to receive the victor's crown of righteousness, which the Lord will hand to me at the Last Day. And since he is a good umpire, he will award the prize, not only to me, but also to all those who have shown a true desire for his appearing.

Do your best to come to me at once. Luke is the only one left with me. Pick up Mark and bring him with you. When you come please bring with you the overcoat I left behind in Troas at Carpus' house. Bring the books too, and don't forget the documents.

At my first cross-examination I had no one to defend me or to vouch for me, but everyone left me severely alone. But the Lord was with me and strengthened me to give a full statement of the gospel in the hearing of all the pagans. So was I rescued from the lion's mouth. The Lord will rescue me from every evil machination and preserve me for his Heavenly Kingdom. His is the glory forever and ever. Amen.

Timothy did not make it in time, nor did Paul need the coat. On his second appearance at the imperial court Paul was condemned to death. "Execution by the sword," was the verdict. In the gray light of early dawn, Paul was led out of the city gate chained between two soldiers. Faithful Luke accompanied him to the place of execution, three miles from the city on the Ostian Way. Paul was old, somewhat stooped; his face was lined with care; he was sick from his imprisonment. But he strode to execution with a vigorous step and the manner of a conqueror. "To leave this world and live with Christ is obviously the best thing," he had once written to his Philippian friends. He believed that, and rejoiced.

As they neared the fatal spot, Paul began to sing one of the martyrs' hymns of the Church:

> "Die we with Christ,
>   And we shall live with Him:
>   Endure all,
>   And with Him we shall reign.

"Deny we Him,
   Ourselves shall be denied—
But seek His love
   'Twill hold in spite of all.

"Dim though our faith,
   The Christ will faithful prove.
We are in Him:
   Himself he cannot fail."

Luke tried to join him but choked and could not sing. Nor could he look, as Paul laid his head on the block, ready for the executioner's sword. Turning, falling on his knees, his head buried in his arms, great sobs shaking his frame, Luke heard Paul's voice once more:

"Die we with Christ,
   And we shall live . . ."

Such was Paul's end—yet not the end. As Luke walked slowly away from the scene, some earlier words of his friend echoed in his ears and set his darkness all aglow: "For to me to live is Christ, and to die is gain."